To: Sir William Staveley, GCB.,DL., Chairman of the North East

Thames Regional Health Authority, and

Mr Peter Barker, Chairman of the South East

Thames Regional Health Authority.

On 27 July 1993 you asked us to inquire into the care and treatment of Christopher Clunis.

We have carried out our investigations and now submit our Report and recommendations.

Jean H. Ritchie

Jean H Ritchie QC (Chairman)

Dr Donald Dick

Richard Lingham.

Richard Lingham

24 February 1994

The Report of the Inquiry into the Care and Treatment of **Christopher Clunis**

ISBN 0 11 701798 1

CONTENTS

SECTION I

1.0. INTRODUCTION

1.1. TERMS OF REFERENCE

1.1.1. The Christopher Clunis Inquiry was set up on 27 July 1993 by the North East Thames and South East Thames Regional Health Authorities. Our terms of reference were as follows:

> 1. To investigate all the circumstances surrounding the admission, treatment, discharge and continuing care of Christopher Clunis between May 1992 and December 1992;
>
> 2. To identify any deficiencies in the quality and delivery of that care, as well as interagency collaboration and individual responsibilities;
>
> 3. To make recommendations for the future delivery of care including admission, treatment, discharge and continuing care to people in similar circumstances so that, as far as possible, harm to patients and the public is avoided.

1.2. METHODS ADOPTED BY THE INQUIRY

1.2.1. At the beginning of our Inquiry we were greatly helped by a letter, dated 2 July 1993, written by Christopher Clunis' Solicitor, Mr Martin Taube of Thanki Novy Taube, to the Secretary of State for Health which set out a detailed chronology; and also by an article in the 19 July 1993 edition of the Independent Newspaper, which had set out their investigations into the case.

1.2.2. We first obtained Christopher Clunis' written consent to our seeing records that related to him. We then asked for copies of all records relating to Christopher Clunis held by any agency we could identify as having had contact with him. This included hospitals, social services departments, housing departments, police stations, the probation service, the Crown Prosecution Service, Crown Courts, hostels for the homeless, and hostels for the mentally ill.

1.2.3. As records were produced they led us to make further enquiries of other institutions, that we had not previously known had had contact with Christopher Clunis. We soon realised that we needed to investigate Christopher Clunis' care before early 1992 if we were to find out the full history of his mental illness and the care he had received. By agreement with the two Regional Health Authorities we extended our inquiries to 1986. The one serious flaw in so doing was that it put back the timing of our report by 2 months. However we felt that in order to carry out our task fully, that was a small penalty.

1.2.4. It was like receiving bits of a jigsaw puzzle, in random order, and trying to find the next piece of the jigsaw so as to allow us to form the picture. We hope that we have now obtained almost all of the documents and that we have now completed the jigsaw puzzle.

1.2.5. As we read the records it became clear that there were a number of factual witnesses from whom we wished to hear evidence. No one refused to appear before us, no one refused to answer questions and all the witnesses of fact were prepared to read a solemn affirmation. We set out in Appendix 1 the full list of witnesses from whom we heard oral evidence and others from whom we received written evidence.

1.2.6. We also received written and oral evidence from a variety of experts, from professional bodies and organisations, and from other interested parties. We set out in Appendix 2 the full list of such witnesses from whom we heard and the Organisations they came from or represented, where appropriate.

1.2.7. We received evidence from 143 witnesses in all. We set out at Appendix 3 a bibliography of source materials.

1.2.8. We first sat to hear evidence on 20 September 1993 and the last day that we heard evidence was on 11 February 1994. We heard all oral evidence at 1 Lower Marsh, London SE1 save for a visit to Rampton Hospital when we interviewed Christopher Clunis and Dr Shubsachs, his Consultant Forensic Psychiatrist. We made one site visit, to Spur House Resettlement Unit, a hostel for the homeless. One witness was not well enough to appear to give oral evidence before us, but he telephoned his views and we subsequently sent him a note of the conversation which he approved.

1.3. OUR THANKS

1.3.1. We wish to extend our thanks to several members of the public who volunteered to give evidence to us about their involvement with Christopher Clunis. We particularly wish to thank Mr Nigel Bartlett who was attacked by Christopher Clunis in the street; Mr and Mrs Hislop with whom he sought refuge; and Mrs Susan Parashar and Miss Angela Esposito J.P., both of whom were so concerned by what they had seen or heard, that they repeatedly contacted the Police to inform them of their concerns. We wish to place on record that the Inquiry is very grateful to them for giving evidence to us.

1.3.2. We have also been greatly indebted to Superintendent Margaret Barker, Superintendent of the Complaints Unit for the area covering Wood Green, Edmonton and Finsbury Park. She was assisted, as were we, by Sergeant Robert Mayhew. We had found enormous difficulty trying to locate which Police Stations had been involved with Christopher Clunis over the years and obtaining records from such stations. It was a huge relief when Superintendent Barker telephoned to say that she would be willing to co-ordinate all the Police information in respect of Christopher Clunis for us. She and Sergeant Mayhew did so. They unearthed documents and interviewed a large number of police officers. They both gave evidence to us. We do not feel that our Inquiry would have been as full or as thorough, if we had not been given such help.

1.3.3. Finally we extend our sincere thanks publicly to Mrs Lesley Warner and to Miss Marie Wilson, who in turn acted as Secretary to the Inquiry. They both gave unstintingly of their time and energy, well beyond the call of duty, and the smooth running of the Inquiry owes much to their endeavours. We also record our thanks to Miss Barbara Watson for her unfailing help throughout the Inquiry.

1.4. PROCEDURE ADOPTED AT OUR SITTINGS

1.4.1. The Inquiry was set up as a private Inquiry. We were mindful of the recent Court of Appeal Judgment in <u>Crampton and others v Secretary of State for Health</u> (the Allitt Inquiry) given on 9th July 1993, and particularly the Judgment of the Master of the Rolls (at pages 22–24 of the Transcript) and therefore before we heard any oral evidence we set out the procedure which we intended to follow. We announced the procedure at the beginning of our sittings on 20 September 1993 in the following terms:

> 1. Every witness of fact will receive a letter in advance of their coming to give evidence informing them:
>
>> (a) of the areas and matters of concern which we wish to cover with them; and
>>
>> (b) that they may bring with them, a friend, relative, member of a trade union, solicitor, or anyone else they wish to accompany them; and
>>
>> (c) that it is the witness who will be asked questions and who will be expected to answer; and
>>
>> (d) that when they come to give oral evidence to us they may raise any matter which they wish to, and which they feel might be relevant to our Inquiry; and
>>
>> (e) that their evidence will be recorded and a copy sent to them afterwards for them to sign.
>
> 2. We shall ask each witness of fact to affirm that his/her evidence is true.
>
> 3. Any points of potential criticism will be put to a witness of fact (either when they first give evidence or, more probably, at a later time) and they will be given a full opportunity to respond.
>
> 4. We have invited representations from professional bodies and other interested parties as to present arrangements for persons in similar circumstances to Christopher Clunis, and as to any recommendations they may have for the future.
>
> 5. We may ask those professional bodies or interested parties to give oral evidence to us about their views and recommendations.
>
> 6. We now invite anyone else who feels they may have something useful to contribute to our Inquiry to make written submissions to us for our consideration.

7. All our sittings will be held in private.

8. The findings of the Inquiry and its recommendations will be made public.

1.4.2. We now add that we shall not make public any of the evidence that has been submitted to us either orally or in writing, save as is disclosed within the body of this Report.

1.4.3. Finally we should make it clear that we make our findings of fact on the basis of the evidence that we have received. Our comments, which appear throughout the narrative, are based on those findings.

1.5. GENERAL OBSERVATIONS

1.5.1. We have tried throughout our investigations, to keep a close eye on any evidence of prejudiced attitudes towards Christopher Clunis. We have asked witnesses for direct and indirect examples of racial discrimination which could have affected his care and treatment. We record that no example of such prejudice or discrimination has become apparent to us, save for the possibility of too great a willingness to accept that he had abused drugs.

1.5.2. It was clear that there is enormous concern about the provision of care in the community for mentally ill people, not just from laymen but from all those involved in caring for the mentally ill in the community. We are of the view that there is a great deal of goodwill amongst people to try and improve the system. We found that most heartening.

1.5.3. However, we were constantly reminded during the course of our Inquiry of the shortcomings in the provision of care in the community for those who suffer from severe mental illness, by the number of reports of such people who regularly appear before the Courts and in the media, as a result of violent incidents carried out when they were being cared for in the community.

1.5.4. We hope that by highlighting some of those shortcomings in the Christopher Clunis case, and by making recommendations, such incidents can be avoided as far as possible in the future.

SECTION II

2.0. THE ZITO FAMILY

2.1. MRS JAYNE ZITO

2.1.1. We heard evidence from Mrs Jayne Zito at the beginning of our Inquiry. She was a most impressive witness. She was quiet, restrained, yet at the same time forceful. She told us of the death of her husband, Mr Jonathan Zito, at the hands of Christopher Clunis on 17 December 1992.

2.1.2. Mrs Jayne Zito told us of how she met and fell in love with Jonathan Zito in Italy in the summer of 1992 and how they were married there on September 12th of the same year. She showed us happy photographs of the wedding celebrations with their families. Soon after the wedding, she returned to London to start postgraduate studies at Middlesex University in Social Work and Social Studies, while Jonathan Zito, who was a professional musician, met touring commitments in Germany, before coming to London on 9th November 1992. They had rented a flat in Hornsey and were setting up their early married life. His family were Italian, but had lived in New York for a number of years before all returning to Italy. They were coming on 17 December 1992 to join Jayne Zito's family for Christmas, in Cornwall, where a cottage had been rented for them all, but were first to spend a few days in London.

2.1.3. She described the events of 17th December 1992; how her husband had gone by car in the morning with a friend to Gatwick Airport to meet his family who were flying in from Pisa; how the family met briefly before setting off to return to Hornsey, Jonathan with his brother by train, and the rest of the family with his friend in the car; how the brothers travelled to Victoria by train and then took a tube to Finsbury Park to change for Turnpike Lane which was the nearest tube station to the flat. Meanwhile Jayne Zito was "waiting for them all to come back but they never came back".

2.1.4. Jayne Zito told us of her background in the residential rehabilitation of mentally ill people in Hertfordshire where she had worked as a Deputy Manager of the Rehabilitation Unit for the Mentally ill. She spoke also of her continuing interest, despite the tragic death of her husband, in the welfare of mentally ill people who have been discharged from hospital.

2.1.5. She described eloquently what she had suffered and of what she had lost; a sensitive, creative, talented and loving husband. Equally she showed real concern for Christopher Clunis, for the terror that he has to face when he considers what he has done, and for the apparent lack of care that he received. She told us that her aim is not to ensure that dangerous or potentially dangerous mentally ill people are locked up. She feels that her husband will not have died in vain if mentally ill patients receive proper care so that they, and the public, are safe.

2.1.6. Her evidence was moving and humbling; she demonstrated huge depths of character and reserve in facing such a tragedy. She brought her husband, Jon, to life for us so that we would know what he and his family, and she and her family, have lost.

2.2. MR VINCENT TUTTON AND MRS IRENE TUTTON

2.2.1. We heard evidence from Mr Vincent Tutton and Mrs Irene Tutton, Jayne Zito's parents. They both described Jonathan Zito as a fine and sensitive young man, whose death had no reason. They have been, and continue to be, a great support to their daughter. They were critical of what they saw as the inadequacies in the system of care which had failed both Jonathan Zito and Christopher Clunis. They wanted us to be sure to keep consideration of the victim, his family and friends in the forefront of our deliberations.

2.3. MR AND MRS ALFRED ZITO

2.3.1. We received written evidence from Mr and Mrs Alfred Zito, Jonathan Zito's parents. They told us how, as Sicilians, their life has always revolved round their family. They spoke of their acute sorrow at the loss of their gentle and talented son. They wanted us to try and ensure that such a tragedy never happened again.

2.4. MISS ALISA ZITO

2.4.1. We also received written evidence from Miss Alisa Zito, Jonathan Zito's sister. She described how close the family has always been and how they have all been devastated by his death. She too expressed the hope that such a tragedy should not happen again.

SECTION III

3.0. THE CHRISTOPHER CLUNIS STORY

3.1. INTRODUCTION

3.1.1 We have learned the following from Christopher Clunis himself, his sister, and from records made by a Nurse at Rampton Hospital after he had I discussed his early life with various members of his family. It is a feature of Christopher Clunis' story that repeatedly, when he was admitted to hospital or was asked about his past history, he gave a version that was entirely unreliable, often showing delusions of grandeur or perceived cleverness. Perhaps it was a symptom of his grandiose ideas that he sometimes used the name Christopher and sometimes the name Allajah, and that sometimes he spelt Clunis with one 'n' and sometimes with two. Throughout the Inquiry we have referred to him as Christopher Clunis. He did not object to our so doing when we went to see him.

3.1.2 On frequent occasions Christopher Clunis told doctors, nurses and social workers that he had abused both hard and soft drugs from an early age; he said he was married at the age of 2; he said he went to Eton College; he said he was born in Sudan. From the investigations we have been able to carry out none of these statements appears to have been true. Indeed there has never been any evidence that he abused drugs, save for his own assertions which then assumed a truth of their own as the statement was repeated from one hospital to another. It was in these circumstances that we have tried to verify as much as possible of his early life and we are very grateful to his sister for coming to speak to us to shed some light on his rather dimly lit history. We do not name her and are happy to respect her privacy.

3.1.3 We should point out that despite some agencies knowing the name and address of his family, they did not make contact either to verify the history he gave or, and perhaps more importantly, to tell them of discharge plans or to discuss his future with them. From the records, we have seen that there were many times when Christopher Clunis would not tell those who were trying to help him, the names and addresses of his family. But there were also many times when he did so, and such addresses were close at hand in the London area. Very few followed up this information.

3.1.4 It came as something of a surprise to learn from his sister that they have maintained contact with him throughout. He kept in touch with them, usually by telephone and they visited from time to time. No member of the family was ever contacted as the Nearest Relative under S 11 Mental Health Act 1983 when he was compulsorily detained. It is clear to us that he came from a supportive and loving family and that they were not involved in his care in a way that would have been helpful to Christopher Clunis.

3.1.5 Accounts of Christopher Clunis frequently refer to his considerable height and powerful build. Yet he was very often referred to as a friendly giant, rather than a threat. The fact that he is articulate and well spoken has perhaps meant that he was not subject to racial stereotyping and preconceptions. On the other hand it was clear from all we have seen and heard that he was determined to pursue his own goals, and he often actively resisted help. It is a feature of the case that we can find not one occasion when Christopher Clunis attended an out patient appointment. We recognise that it would be difficult for Doctors and Social Workers to counter such a combination of physical presence, verbal strength and fierce determination on the part of any patient. The added factor of his blackness may have contributed to the diffident manner in which some professionals treated him, and it may have caused them to defer, against his best interests, to his own expressed wishes

COMMENT

3.1.6 *Health and social services workers took few, if any, steps to contact members of his family, and thereby they lost touch with some of the basic realities of his personal history, as well as losing the family's potentially valuable support in his treatment and aftercare. They treated him as single, homeless, and itinerant with no family ties, and the more they treated him as such the more he began to fulfil that role. Too often his refusal to allow access to his family to those who were caring for him, was accepted without further question or investigation, even though family members had rights to be consulted regarding his detention under the Mental Health Act 1983.*

3.2. FROM BIRTH IN 1963 UNTIL HE LEFT SCHOOL IN 1980

3.2.1 Christopher Clunis was born on 18 May 1963 in Muswell Hill, London N10. His parents both came from Jamaica. He had 4 half brothers and sisters on his father's side and 1 half brother on his mother's side. He was the youngest of all the children and the only child of his parents' union. He went to nursery school in Hornsey and in 1968 the family moved to Luton where Christopher Clunis completed his primary school education and his parents were able to marry. His father worked for the Vauxhall Motor Company in Luton for many years until he retired. Christopher Clunis then attended secondary school in Luton obtaining O levels in at least Mathematics, English and Geography and probably 3 more. He went to sixth form college and to Luton Technical College where he studied for A levels in economics and sociology. His sister felt he was quite clever and used to enjoy reading and going to the library. However his real and abiding interest was in music and, in particular, jazz. He played the guitar, and he gave up his studies to follow a musical career. The books he read tended to be about music.

3.2.2 His father noticed that when he was young he had a liking for knives. It was not something his sister noticed, but their father had definitely noted such a propensity.

3.3. FROM 1980 TO 1985

3.3.1 In 1980 Christopher Clunis' mother suffered a stroke and his parents went to live in Jamaica. At that time he was noted to have become untidy and had poor personal habits. However his musical career then took off, he played with a group called the Aqua Vita Showband and they travelled abroad. His sister told us "he loved it."

When he was away he contacted her from time to time, generally on the telephone. He returned to England from time to time and lived in Luton, near to where he had lived with his parents. Then he went to live in Hornsey. He was registered with a General Practitioner in Enfield in 1984. That was Dr Subrahmanyam from whom we have heard evidence.

3.3.2 Christopher Clunis joined Dr Subrahmanyam's practice list on 12 July 1984. He saw Christopher Clunis just once, on 10 July 1984 for a matter not related to his psychiatric state. His previous General Practitioner notes had apparently gone missing so that a new card was created for him. We have seen no medical records for the period between Christopher Clunis' birth and July 1984.

3.3.4 Despite Christopher Clunis' frequent admissions to hospital thereafter Dr Subrahmanyam never received any communication or discharge summary from any of those Hospitals or from anyone else. On occasions Christopher Clunis gave the name and address of his General Practitioner to hospitals where he was admitted. We heard evidence from Dr Subrahmanyam who told us "I never heard from anyone".

3.3.5 It appears to be at that stage, sometime in 1984, that Christopher Clunis had a girl friend whose parents came from India. His sister told us that the girl's family did not like the idea of her going out with Christopher Clunis and when they began to live together her family took her away and sent her to India. She felt that had a profound effect on her brother.

3.3.6 Christopher Clunis then went abroad again and while he was away in 1985 his mother died. He did not learn of her death until he returned to England so that he did not know when she died nor did he attend the funeral, which the rest of the family attended in Jamaica. He learned of her death when his sister told him on the telephone. She had not wanted to do so on the telephone and had asked him to come and visit her for a chat. But he said he was too busy, so that it was in those circumstances that she told him over the 'phone. That seems also to have had a profound effect on him. He would never discuss the matter with his sister and he never discussed his mother again with her.

3.4. 1986 – ADMISSION TO BELLEVUE HOSPITAL, JAMAICA

3.4.1 Christopher Clunis began to show signs of odd behaviour and in 1986 he turned up at one of his brothers' home. His sister told us that she went to see him and he was dressed inappropriately for the cold weather and he was rambling. She felt he was obviously ill. She took him home with her for a couple of weeks and then suddenly, out of the blue, while the family were watching television together, he attempted to hit one of his nieces when she changed the programme. Christopher Clunis' sister told us that her brother had a strange look when this took place. She was very worried. She contacted their father who suggested that his son join him in Jamaica. She paid for his fare.

3.4.2 After his arrival in Jamaica he continued to behave oddly and did not look after himself properly. We understand that he was admitted to Bellevue Hospital, Windward Road, Kingston, Jamaica when he was diagnosed as having paranoid schizophrenia. We have tried, as have others, to obtain the records from that hospital but without success. A Clinical Nurse Specialist from Rampton Hospital went to Jamaica as a Churchill Fellow in June 1993 . She visited the Bellevue Hospital in order to try and obtain the records, and despite promises to produce them nothing ever was disclosed. Our efforts have met with total silence. After he was discharged he went to live with his father but his father became ill and Christopher Clunis returned to England.

3.5. RETURN TO ENGLAND – 1987

3.5.1 In early 1987 Christopher Clunis returned to live in England and went to stay with one of his sisters in Birmingham. Further episodes of bizarre behaviour were observed. Then one day in April 1987 he suddenly left his sister's home and the Birmingham area without even telling her. He came back to live in London. We have not been able to find out where, although Christopher Clunis told us he lived at a friend's flat.

3.5.2 By June 1987 he was in contact with his other sister again. He was found by her in Wood Green in a terrible state. She took him to the Accident and Emergency department of Chase Farm Hospital. He returned to her home and she describes him standing and gazing at nothing for long periods of time. He would sit in the back room with the curtains drawn and no lights on, smoking. He collected rubbish in a black sack and sat with it.

3.5.3 Christopher Clunis' sister impressed us as a warm and caring person who told us that she had maintained contact with her brother throughout. It is clear that she did so, visiting him, sometimes with her own children, at several of the hostels where he lived and at several of the hospitals to which he was admitted over the years. Sometimes he put up a barrier to questions and if she persisted he became annoyed. He would ring her from time to time and she would ask him if she could bring any-thing for him when she visited. Occasionally she sent him money and there is certainly one note we have come across during the investigation where the fact that he received money from his sister was recorded in the medical notes.

3.5.4 Sometimes, she told us, she found he was in a reasonable state but at other times he seemed very uncared for. She said she just could not look after him herself with her own work and family commitments but she felt he needed a lot more super-vision and a lot more care and attention. She had good insight; she told us, "Even when he seemed OK, deep down I think that he wasn't." She felt the various caring services should have helped him but "instead of that he was just left to his own devices and that was rather sad." She felt that she and her family had not been given the help they needed. "I think it would have helped if we had had some support or guidance". She had never been introduced to a Support Group.

3.5.5 She told us that his brothers also visited him occasionally but the family had always kept in contact in some way. Generally they had to wait for him to ring them because he moved about so much. However as she told us, "we were always there for him" and he knew that. She thought the last official communication she had received about her brother was from Lambeth Social Services in about 1991.

10

4.0. CHASE FARM HOSPITAL

4.1.1 THE FIRST VISIT – 29 JUNE 1987

4.1.2 Christopher Clunis first attended Chase Farm Hospital, The Ridgeway, Enfield, Middlesex on 29th June 1987 when he was taken to the Accident and Emergency department by his sister. According to his sister he was in a terrible state, filthy, underweight, uncommunicative, confused, disorientated, staring into space, laughing and giggling to himself. He was seen by the Duty Psychiatrist, Dr Cohen, who took a full history from Christopher Clunis and his sister and formed the impression that Christopher Clunis was a schizophrenic with negative features. Since he refused inpatient or day patient admission the duty psychiatrist advised that he should be assessed urgently by Dr Fernando's team. Dr Fernando was at that time a Consultant Psychiatrist with responsibility for the sector of Enfield in which Christopher Clunis' sister lived. We have heard evidence from Dr Fernando who has now retired from practice.

4.1.3 On the same day a member of Dr Fernando's team, the Community Psychiatric Nurse visited Christopher Clunis at his sister's home. A further home visit was made on 1 July 1987 when his sister expressed concerns at his lack of housing, the strain on her family of having him in the house and the possibility that he might become aggressive.

4.2. THE SECOND VISIT – 2 JULY 1987 TO 27 JULY 1987

4.2.1 He was seen again at Chase Farm Hospital on 2 July 1987 by the Duty Psychiatrist, having fallen and lost consciousness for a few minutes. It was recorded that he "has become destitute and living rough", that he was sleeping for most of the day, was virtually mute and unable to care for himself. He gave a history of drug abuse. The Duty Doctor considered that he was likely to be suffering from a schizophrenic illness. He was admitted to hospital for assessment when it was thought his illness might be drug induced or schizophrenic. With treatment his condition had much improved by 15 July 1987.

4.2.2 On 21 July 1987 he left the ward without permission and on his return he was noted to be elated and vague. It was thought he might have been abusing drugs in his absence from hospital and a urine sample was taken. It was felt that he probably had a drug induced psychosis. However when the drug screen was finally reported on 18 August 1987 it was then found to be negative. On 24 July 1987 he was noted to be overfamiliar and rude to female staff and patients. It was decided to discharge him and to assist him with finding accommodation. No out patient appointment was recorded as having been given given and, since he was said to have no General Practitioner, there was no arrangement for any follow up care. We have not been able to discover whether he was given any help with his accommodation before the Housing Department at Enfield Civic Centre telephoned the Hospital on 24 August 1987 to ask for a report on Christopher Clunis. In a letter dated 26 August 1987 to the Housing department Dr Rupasinghe said that the diagnosis was either mental illness or drug induced psychosis or a combination of both. He stated that he was capable of living on his own and would not be a danger to himself.

4.2.3 Dr Fernando told us that in his view Christopher Clunis was probably suffering from a degree of depression, since he had never fully recovered from the death of his mother. In his view in treating black people, depression is often missed as a diagnosis but drug induced psychosis is too frequently ascribed. Dr Fernando had been away on extended leave during the summer of 1987 and so had not seen Christopher Clunis on either of the first two visits to Chase Farm Hospital and in fact only ever saw Christopher Clunis once. He thought that there was reduced supervision of junior staff in his absence.

4.2.4 Christopher Clunis' sister felt that he had been discharged too early, before he had really become settled. She told us that he seemed happy when he was in Chase Farm Hospital. He was not left to wander off. He felt safe. Also the Hospital was situated in the country and she felt he enjoyed that environment.

4.3. THE THIRD VISIT – 13 DECEMBER 1987 TO 17 DECEMBER 1987

4.3.1 Christopher Clunis attended the Accident and Emergency department of Chase Farm Hospital again on 13 December 1987 when he was accompanied by his sister and a social worker. We have not been able to discover who the social worker was or from which department he/she came. Christopher Clunis' mental state had apparently deteriorated sharply during the previous week and he was reported to be unkempt, subdued, and asked his niece if she were a ghost. He had lost his accommodation 2 weeks previously. He was seen in casualty in an unkempt and dirty condition with a bedspread over one shoulder and a tyre over the other. He said he had not slept for days and wanted to sleep. The Duty Psychiatrist wondered whether he was putting on symptoms in order to gain admission although it was noted that he had resisted attempts to attend the Accident and Emergency department until his sister had threatened to call the police. It was decided to admit him briefly. On 15 December 1987 he was noted to be masturbating on the ward and entering female dormitories. He refused to answer questions and would not give a urine sample. By 17 December 1987 on treatment he was found to be very settled with no evidence of any psychotic symptoms. He was discharged, the diagnosis being a transient psychotic state induced either by drugs or as a reaction to situational crises. He refused any social work help and his family were not contacted. No outpatient appointment was made and since it was still thought that he had no General Practitioner there was no arrangement for any follow up care. Neither was his family contacted.

4.4. THE FOURTH VISIT – 1 JANUARY 1988 TO 4 JANUARY 1988

4.4.1 On I January 1988 Christopher Clunis was taken to the Casualty department by the Police under S. 136 Mental Health Act 1983. He had been seen by a member of the public sitting on a motorcycle in Tottenham. He refused to say anything other than to give his name and address. On examination by the Duty Psychiatrist his mood was very flat. He was admitted and the impression was that he was suffering from a drug induced state, or a psychotic state of other origin or that he was manipulating his condition to gain admission. Later that day he struck a fellow patient for taking his cigarettes. He would not comply with any investigations. On the following day he kicked a patient for no reason. He improved dramatically on medication and Dr Karri diagnosed "drug induced ? psychosis with no fixed abode". On 4 January 1988 he took his own discharge against medical advice. The ward records state that no social worker had been to interview him during the 72 hour period of detention permitted by S.136, despite the request of the Hospital staff that one should do so. We understand however that Peter Finch was told by the duty psychiatrist that she had no decided whether to admit Christopher Clunis informerly or to detain him for assessment, and that she would contact Peter Finch if she decided to detain him. Peter Finch heard no more. Once again no outpatient appointment was given and since he had no General Practitioner no arrangements for any follow up were made.

4.5. THE FIFTH VISIT – 4 FEBRUARY 1988 TO 8 FEBRUARY 1988

4.5.1 Christopher Clunis attended the Casualty department voluntarily and on his own on 4 February 1988. He was in a poor state with very dirty clothing, flat affect and poverty of thought. He wanted a bed for the night. The Duty Psychiatrist considered that he was suffering from a defect state schizophrenia. He agreed to cooperate and was admitted to Dorset ward. The following day he refused to answer questions and it was noted that there was no evidence of any psychiatric illness. He was quietly cooperative over the next two days and was seen by the Hospital Social Worker who helped him to find accommodation. He was discharged on 8 February 1988. No follow up care was arranged.

4.6. POLICE INVOLVEMENT MARCH 1988

4.6.1 It appears that Christopher Clunis was in Her Majesty's Prison Brixton on 15 March 1988 but we do not know why or how he came to be released. Our investigations have drawn a blank on this episode. HMP Brixton wrote to Chase Farm Hospital on 15 March 1988 asking for details of Christopher Clunis care at that Hospital. Dr Fernando replied to HMP Brixton on 8 April 1988 sending information and enclosures about Christopher Clunis to the Prison.

4.7. THE SIXTH AND FINAL VISIT TO CHASE FARM –
29 MARCH 1988

4.7.1 On 29 March 1988 Christopher Clunis attended the Casualty department once again asking to be admitted as he had nowhere to live. He would not allow a physical examination nor would he provide a urine sample. The Duty Psychiatrist considered the differential diagnoses to be a psychotic or schizoaffective illness. He did not consider that his mental state required admission to the acute psychotic ward but there were several attempts to contact the duty social worker. We were informed in a letter from Enfield Social Services Department that they had made contact with Christopher Clunis in March 1988, and had given him some advice relating to housing. Christopher Clunis was allowed to stay in the Casualty department visiting room overnight and given the address of the department of Health and Social Security in Edmonton. No contact was made or apparently attempted with his General Practitioner or his family.

4.8. COMMENT

4.8.1 *We are very concerned that each episode of illness was treated separately, rather than as part of a continuing illness. A conclusive diagnosis was not made, although on several occasions schizophrenia was considered as the diagnosis. Christopher Clunis was treated almost as though he were a new patient, on each of his 6 admissions and attendances. No proper response was made to his obvious need for help; little support or help was given to his family; any referral that was made to Social Services was not pursued. There is a direct conflict of evidence regarding his referral for social work help, but the correspondence from Enfield Social Services suggests that offers of help made by the approved social worker were not taken up by the hospital staff. The opportunity was lost to treat him in the area where he had family connections and with which he was familiar. No long term planning for his care in the community was considered or made. Above all the opportunity for early diagnosis and possibly effective treatment of schizophrenia was lost.*

4.8.2 We are worried that little help or aftercare was given to Christopher Clunis over a period of 8 months in respect of his accommodation and treatment, despite his frequent relapses and his obvious continuing need. He and his family clearly needed support and guidance. They received little save when he was in an acute stage of his illness. Dr Fernando now recognises this, and appears to agree with us that Christopher Clunis had not received, over the 8 month period, the full support, care and treatment which he needed.

5.0. POLICE INVOLVEMENT

5.1. 26 APRIL 1988

5.1.1 Within a month of his last contact with Chase Farm Hospital Christopher Clunis was in trouble with the Police. On 26 April 1988 he was arrested in West Green Road, Tottenham, London and was charged with stealing two loaves of bread which he had tried to stuff down his trousers. He was taken to St Anne's Road Police Station and remanded to HMP Brixton. He appeared at Highgate Magistrates' Court on 27 April 1988 when he was remanded on bail to a bail hostel. Apparently there was no space available in the local bail hostel at Highgate so he was taken to a Probation Hostel at 147, Tulse Hill, Brixton, London SE27. He was due to appear in Court again on 3 May 1988.

5.2 COMMENT

5.2.1 We observe that although Christopher Clunis' offence occurred in Tottenham and his home area was in North London, he was sent away to South London. He was at that time suffering from a severe mental illness, and the change of residence meant that he was disturbed even further, taking him from the environment with which he was familiar and from his family, to an area with which he was totally unfamiliar and with which he had no connection. We find it hard to believe that no placement in a bail hostel could be found nearer than Tulse Hill.

6.0. KING'S COLLEGE AND DULWICH NORTH HOSPITALS

6.1. KING'S COLLEGE HOSPITAL – 26 APRIL 1988 TO 3 MAY 1988

6.1.1 Christopher Clunis was seen as an out patient on 26 April 1988 at the Emergency Clinic, King's College Hospital, Denmark Hill, London SE5 by Dr Berti, (Registrar to Dr Gaius Davies, Consultant Psychiatrist) having been brought there by a probation officer from Tulse Hill Probation Hostel. He was noted to be talking to himself and laughing, refusing to eat or drink, making inappropriate contact with females and exposing himself. He refused to answer questions and Dr Berti considered that he was psychotic and required admission for assessment and treatment. However no bed was available and therefore he was discharged back to the hostel on medication and asked to return the next day. He was reviewed the next day when his condition remained the same, further medication was prescribed, and he was asked to return again the following day.

6.1.2 No further notes were available to us until 3 May 1988 but it appears that Christopher Clunis remained at the Probation Hostel until 3 May 1988 and that he might well have been seen at the Emergency Clinic on a daily basis during that time. He was due to appear on 3 May 1988 before the Highgate Magistrates' Court, and the Probation Officer told Dr Berti that unless he could be admitted to Hospital he would be sent to prison. A bed then seems to have been made available in Dulwich North Hospital and therefore, when Christopher Clunis appeared before the Magistrates' Court, he was remanded until 25 May 1988 on unconditional bail on the basis that he would be admitted to Hospital. He was assessed thereafter at the Emergency Clinic, King's College Hospital and was then admitted to Dulwich North Hospital on 3 May 1988.

6.1.3 We have heard evidence from Dr Gaius Davies, Consultant Psychiatrist at King's College and Dulwich North Hospitals. He seemed to us a concerned psychiatrist who had tried to give of his best over the years but had become increasingly disillusioned with the Health Service and the provision for the mentally ill. He told us that he was glad to be retiring but he still wanted to tell us of ideas he had to change the system for the better.

6.2. DULWICH NORTH HOSPITAL – 3 MAY 1988 TO 12 MAY 1988

6.2.1 Christopher Clunis was admitted to Dulwich North Hospital, St Francis Road, London SE22 on 3 May 1988 and was seen by the Duty Doctor. He refused to answer questions or to give a history and would only agree to a partial examination. He was described as dishevelled, dirty, smelly, looking puzzled and bewildered at times, apparently responding to internal stimuli, turning his head suddenly, at other times mumbling to himself, with very poor eye contact and rapport. The Doctor considered that he might be suffering from (i) schizophrenia, (ii) drug induced psychosis or (iii) an organic illness.

6.2.2 He was assessed by Dr Walsh on 5 May 1988 when she found him unforthcoming and considered he might be giving misleading information. She noted he was sexually provocative and disinhibited. After a determined effort to investigate his past, Dr Walsh appears to have been told by Dr Sammutt from Chase Farm Hospital that Christopher Clunis had been in Chase Farm Hospital four times within the previous 6 months and that they had considerable doubt as to the diagnosis of schizophrenia and overall thought that he was a difficult young man who just wanted a bed. He appears to have indicated that the Hospital was unwilling to take responsibility for him because they did not regard him as psychotic.

6.2.3 On 6 May 1988 a nurse recorded that he was quite agitated and was found walking around with a hospital cutlery knife in his pocket which he only reluctantly handed back. Over the next few days he was noted to be argumentative and irritable and on 8 May 1988 threatened violence. On 10 May 1988 he was noted to be abusive and threatening to the nursing staff. Also on 10 May 1988 Dr Walsh found his mental state normal but noted he had behavioural problems rather than psychiatric problems. On 11 May 1988 he became very angry with another patient for no apparent reason and pushed the patient very hard so that he was thrown across the floor.

6.2.4 On 12 May it was decided he was fit for discharge. Dr Davies told us that the ward was old and Dickensian and that violence was commonplace. In his view it was totally unsuitable for the care of the mentally ill and as a result patients were discharged sooner than they might otherwise have been.

6.2.5 On 13 May 1988 Antoni Korris, Social Worker at Dulwich North, gave Christopher Clunis a letter to take to the Homeless Persons Unit, Lambeth, and an outpatient appointment was made for him to see Dr Walsh at Dulwich North on 13 July 1988. It was decided to send a discharge summary to Dr Fernando at Chase Farm Hospital but that does not seem to have been done and in fact no discharge summary at all appears in the notes. We have not been able to discover where Christopher Clunis lived after his discharge from Dulwich North but it may well have been in bed and breakfast accommodation provided by Lambeth Social services. In the event he suffered a relapse within 12 days of his discharge.

6.3. COMMENT

6.3.1 *It seems to us that the pressure to discharge patients from a Dickensian ward may have taken precedence over the health and well being of Christopher Clunis. He was clearly not ready to be discharged into the community, hence he relapsed within so short a time. No plan was made for his future care; no discharge summary was sent to his General Practitioner or to Dr Fernando at Chase Farm Hospital, both of whom might have been expected to care for him in the future; and there was no attempt to re-introduce him either to his home environment north of the river, or to his family. He was treated as a single, homeless man who was simply referred for help with accommodation to the Homeless Persons Unit. However we understand that Dr davies and his team were working in very difficult conditions which made the minimum of decent care almost impossible to maintain.*

7.0. POLICE INVOLVEMENT

7.1. 25 MAY 1988

7.1.1 On 25 May 1988 Christopher Clunis broke into the home of an elderly lady on the Wyril Estate, London SW8, and was found in her bathroom. There was nothing to suggest he was trying to steal, or to commit any other offence. He was arrested and was taken to Clapham Police Station. He was charged with criminal damage to the front door of the property and appeared at South Western Magistrates' Court on 25 May 1988 when he was remanded in custody until 15 June 1988. At that time prisoners were being kept in custody all over the country because of an industrial dispute in the prison service, and Christopher Clunis was taken to Doncaster Police Station and detained there. No psychiatric report was prepared there and the Probation Officer, who travelled up to Doncaster to see him was unable to complete his enquiries by 15 June 1988. The Probation Officer asked for an adjournment but requested that Christopher Clunis should receive treatment in the meantime. He was remanded to HMP Brixton.

7.2. COMMENT

7.2.1 We observe that the Police clearly considered this offence as one of concern. We agree. Breaking into the home of an elderly lady was no doubt a very frightening experience for her and it was right, in our view, that Christopher Clunis was charged. It was the last time until his arrest for murder that Christopher Clunis was charged with any offence (save for one for breach of the peace) despite, as we shall refer to below, a whole series of violent attacks by him over the ensuing 4 years.

8.0. HMP BRIXTON

8.1. 5 JULY 1988 TO 26 JULY 1988

8.1.1 Dr Davies visited Christopher Clunis at HMP Brixton on 5 July 1988 at the request of Dr Alexander, Senior Medical Officer to the Prison. Dr Davies wrote a very full letter to Dr Alexander on 12 July 1988 in which he stated that the diagnosis was "a paranoid schizophrenic illness in someone who has an unusual personality and who has been unable to cope, and perhaps has not been given the full benefits of community care." He described the history he obtained from Christopher Clunis as " wholly unreliable and may well be evidence of his grandiose delusions." He doubted whether he had ever abused drugs and doubted a diagnosis of drug-induced psychosis. Dr Davies commented that Christopher Clunis was uncooperative and sexually disinhibited. He recommended a Hospital Order under S.37 Mental Health Act 1983 and said that he would be willing to provide a bed on such a disposal.

8.1.2 Christopher Clunis was made the subject of a S.37 Order by the South Western Magistrates' Court on 13 July 1988. Pursuant thereto he was admitted to Dulwich North Hospital on 26 July 1988 and Dr Davies was named as his Responsible Medical Officer.

8.1.3 As Christopher Clunis had failed to appear at Highgate Magistrates' Court on 25 May 1988 a warrant was issued for his arrest. That was withdrawn on 10 August 1988 and the charge against him regarding theft of bread was dropped because the Crown Prosecution Service were by then aware that a S 37 Mental Health Act 1983 Order had been made on 13 July 1988 at the South Western Magistrates' Court.

8.2. COMMENT

8.2.1 We observe that between 25 May 1988 and 5 July 1988, a period of 6 weeks, no psychiatric assessment was made on Christopher Clunis. We consider that such a delay meant that he was not provided with the care and treatment that he required.

9.0. DULWICH NORTH HOSPITAL

9.1. 26 JULY 1988 TO 11 AUGUST 1988

9.1.1 Dr Fernando wrote to Dr Davies on 20 July 1988 sending some information about Christopher Clunis' history and suggesting that he should be considered to be within Dulwich North Hospital's catchment area for help and care in hospital or in the community. A copy of that letter is not now within the Dulwich North notes, although below the clinical entry dated 18 July 1988, there is a note, written by Dr Davies, which refers to a letter from Dr Fernando. In our view it is likely that Dr

Fernando's letter was received at Dulwich North Hospital but that it has since gone missing from the file. On 4 August 1988 Dr Euba (Registrar to Dr Davies) wrote to Chase Farm Hospital asking for Christopher Clunis' clinical records. Dr Fernando sent copies of the Chase Farm clinical records to Dr Euba on 17 August 1988 but again those notes do not presently appear in the Dulwich North Hospital file. We have no way of knowing whether they were ever received, whether they were ever put in Christopher Clunis' file or whether they have subsequently gone missing.

9.1.2 On admission Christopher Clunis was noted to have poor self care with side effects from medication, and to be smiling constantly. His talk was monotonous and with poor content. He had grandiose delusions and no insight. The nursing records indicate that he was rude and abusive in the first few days of his admission. On medication he improved rapidly and he was discharged from the S.37 Mental Health Act 1983 Order on 11 August 1988, and from Hospital to bed and breakfast accommodation on the following day. He was apparently given an outpatient appointment and an arrangement was made for him to attend the depot clinic for injections. The discharge summary written by Dr Euba and dated 6 September 1988 stated that the diagnosis was possibly behaviour problems and possibly schizophrenia. The prognosis was said to be poor. Dr Davies told us that in his view Christopher Clunis was suffering from paranoid schizophrenia and he disagreed with Dr Euba's provisional diagnoses.

9.1.3 It is clear that Dulwich Hospital North by then knew the name and address of Christopher Clunis' then General Practitioner, Dr Subrahmanyam, but a copy of the discharge summary does not seem to have been sent to him as Dr Subrahmanyam had none in his records.

9.2. SOCIAL SERVICES INVOLVEMENT

9.2.1 Christopher Clunis was seen by the part time Psychiatric Social Worker at Dulwich North who was William Horder. He wrote on 12 August 1988 to the Homeless Persons Adviser at the Housing Department, Lambeth Town Hall describing Christopher Clunis as vulnerable and difficult to help, who was unlikely to return of his own volition but would probably be brought back by the police in the near future. He described Christopher Clunis' problems as "long term", but said that he had not presented any behaviour problems on the ward.

9.2.2 William Horder also contacted Christopher Clunis' sister who expressed her concern that he could not cope without supervision. She told him he was a drifter whom it was difficult to follow in the community. William Horder described her as a concerned and helpful person who had found caring for Christopher Clunis a great strain in the past. We agree with that assessment. Christopher Clunis was placed by the Homeless Persons Unit at the Carmarthen Hotel, 35 Norfolk Place London W2. This, we understand, was bed and breakfast accommodation.

9.2.3 On 9 September 1988 Christopher Clunis returned to Dulwich North Hospital for an injection where he also saw William Horder. He described him as a vulnerable homeless man but said that "there is no focus of work at present" and so discharged him from his care.

9.3 COMMENT

9.3.1 *It is noteworthy that Christopher Clunis was discharged from Hospital within 16 days, far less time than it had taken to give him a psychiatric assessment. He was treated again as a homeless person and no contact was made with the Social Services in the area which he considered his home. No discharge summary was sent to his General Practitioner. No plan was made for his care or follow up in the community, despite his sister's view that he needed supervision and despite the fact that his prognosis was poor.*

9.3.2 *We are of the view that Christopher Clunis was entitled to a greater degree of care from Dr Davies and his team at Dulwich North Hospital at that time. He had been admitted under S 37 Mental Health Act 1983 and the Hospital was required to provide S 117 aftercare.*

9.3.3 *Furthermore we do not understand how the Psychiatric Social Worker could have come to the view that Christopher Clunis had not presented any behaviour problems on the ward, since the clinical and nursing records, in respect of his 2 inpatient admissions, described his violent and disturbed behaviour. The Social Worker could not have read the medical and nursing records or discussed the case with the staff. It seems to be an example of the desire not to stigmatise a patient, or label him in any way as a violent or difficult person, which it was felt might work to his disadvantage. While we understand the humanitarian considerations that may prompt this attitude, we find that time and time again a failure to assess properly or to describe his condition properly did not present an accurate picture to those who came to care for him afterwards, which ultimately served Christopher Clunis very badly.*

9.3.4 *We have been unable to discover, despite our investigations, where Christopher Clunis lived or what treatment he received between September 1988 and April 1989. During all that time he should have been receiving careful planned aftercare under S 117 Mental Health Act 1983. He was effectively lost to the Health and Social Services for 7 months.*

10.0. LAMBETH HOUSING SERVICES

10.1. MANOR COURT CHAMBERS APRIL 1989 TO JUNE 1989

10.1.1 At some stage, but we have been unable to discover when, Christopher Clunis was accommodated at Manor Court Chambers, 7 Clanricard Gardens, London W2 which was bed and breakfast accommodation provided by Lambeth Housing Services. His sister visited him there and she said it was not a very nice place. She described his room as "a tiny little attic" which she did not think was at all suitable. She told us "it was just terrible".

10.1.2 Jenny Norville, Special Needs Housing Officer in Lambeth Social Services, was responsible, with the Homeless Single Persons' Team, for the housing needs of Christopher Clunis at this time. We have not heard evidence from Jenny Norville but we have seen her detailed records and were impressed by them. We have however heard evidence from Mr Hugh Murray, Resettlement Worker in the Homeless Single Persons' Team of Lambeth Social Services Department. He was in contact with Christopher Clunis between 5 May 1989 and 23 July 1991, the longest period (as far as we have been able to discover) that any single person, other than a relative, had contact with Christopher Clunis. We were impressed by Hugh Murray; he seemed to us conscientious and compassionate. We feel that he did much to help Christopher Clunis over a long period of time and in difficult circumstances. We also heard from Michael Bryant, Homeless Single Persons' Team Leader in Lambeth Social Services whom we found impressive.

10.1.3 On 20 April 1989 Jenny Norville visited Christopher Clunis at Manor Court Chambers when he told her that he did not like living in bed and breakfast accommodation. She felt he needed supported accommodation and suggested that the Jeffrey's Road Hostel might be suitable. She described him as "polite with a nice personality", noted that there was no history of violence, and referred to the psychiatric social worker's report from Dulwich Hospital which had said there were no behavioural problems on the ward. She felt he needed a stable and secure place to live for otherwise he might relapse. As we now know from our investigations, Christopher Clunis had threatened violence and on occasions had used violence on others. Jenny Norville knew none of that history, and by contrast received reports positively asserting that he had no history of violence.

10.2. INTERVIEW AT JEFFREY'S ROAD HOSTEL — 5 MAY 1989

10.2.1 Jenny Norville took Christopher Clunis to be interviewed at Jeffrey's Road on 5 May 1989 but she was concerned that as they were walking to the Hostel he seemed to be hearing voices. He was interviewed at Jeffrey's Road by a member of the staff at Jeffrey's Road and by Hugh Murray, the Resettlement Officer from the Homeless Single Persons' Team. Christopher Clunis apparently spoke very well, liked the accommodation and was accepted to live there. He was however very anxious and Jenny Norville again thought he was hearing voices. Christopher Clunis did not take up the offer of accommodation at Jeffrey's Road.

10.2.2 On 12 May 1989 the Manager of Manor Court Chambers, where he continued to live, said Christopher Clunis was causing problems and would not leave his room. The other residents were reported to be afraid of him as he was becoming quite violent. Jenny Norville tried to contact Christopher Clunis but without success. She arranged with Hugh Murray to make a joint visit on 22 May 1989. In the meantime she contacted the Psychiatric Social Worker, William Horder, who felt that Christopher Clunis might be suffering a relapse. He advised that Christopher Clunis be treated as soon as possible.

10.2.3 Jenny Norville and Hugh Murray saw Christopher Clunis on 22 May 1989 when they noted that he was obviously ill and that he accepted that he needed treatment. However he would not go with them to Hospital. Hugh Murray described him as suffering from thought disorder, with delusional ideas, and described Christopher Clunis' telling him that he had carried out an operation on his jugular vein himself, then laughing inappropriately. Jenny Norville set out in her records that Christopher Clunis put his hands round Jenny Norville's neck from behind and Hugh Murray warned him to behave. Hugh Murray was of the view that he was ill but not sectionable. They decided to return to see him again later in the week. It has to be remembered that as far as they both knew, Christopher Clunis had no history of violence.

10.3. SOCIAL SERVICES CONTACT WITH ST CHARLES' HOSPITAL 23 MAY 1989 TO 7 JUNE 1989

10.3.1 Hugh Murray discussed the case with Michael Bryant (Team Leader of the Homeless Single Persons' Team). Michael Bryant telephoned St Charles' Hospital on 23 May 1989 when we believe that he suggested the need for a Domiciliary Visit by a doctor. Jenny Norville also contacted St Charles' Hospital who said that he would have to be assessed by the Community Assessment Team and that he would be sent an appointment. Jenny Norville pointed out that he would be very unlikely to respond if he were given such an appointment, and said that he needed a Domiciliary Visit. She was given the names of Dr Roth and Dr Higgit. However no Domiciliary Visit took place at that time. On 25 May 1989 Hugh Murray rang St Charles' and was told that Dr Roth was away. He stressed the urgency of the matter. Dr Roth telephoned Hugh Murray on 31 May 1989 and said he would carry out a Domiciliary Visit before the end of the week. We have heard evidence from Dr Roth. He told us that he visited Christopher Clunis once but could not gain access. He did not make a record of that visit. He also told us that Dr Lambert, the Senior Registrar, also visited and could not gain entry either. He said it was a real problem finding time to do a Domiciliary Visit in between one's clinical duties at the Hospital. He said there was no request for an emergency assessment.

10.3.2 On 6 June 1989 Hugh Murray rang St Charles' to find out whether a visit had taken place. Dr Roth telephoned him back on 7 June 1989 and said that Christopher Clunis had been visited twice, but access could not be gained to his room. Dr Roth intended to return on Friday 9 June 1989 with an Approved Social Worker or to use S 135 Mental Health Act 1983 powers. Before that could take place Christopher Clunis was arrested by the Police.

10.3.3 Apparently Lambeth Council had to carry out work at Manor Court Chambers because of fire regulations and on 6 June 1989 required all the residents to move out, arranging for them to be housed elsewhere. This all seems to us rather sudden but as we have not heard direct evidence about this matter we will make no further comment. On 6 June 1989 Christopher Clunis would not leave his room and bolted himself in. A member of staff tried to climb into the room via the window but Christopher Clunis attacked him. After an hour Christopher Clunis left his room but then attacked the Manager by putting his hands round the Manager's throat. They were separated by a hotel worker and Christopher Clunis burst into laughter. The Police do not appear to have been informed at that stage.

10.4. COMMENT

10.4.1 *In our view there was a failure by Social Services to respond quickly enough to the report that Christopher Clunis was becoming violent. No visit was made by Social Workers until 10 days after they were notified of his violence. Then the Consultant Psychiatrist at St Charles' Hospital failed to ensure that he was assessed at a Domiciliary Visit quickly enough. No visit was made for 14 days after the Hospital was informed that such a visit was required. The delay between 12 May 1989 and the proposed Domiciliary Visit with an Approved Social Worker on 9 June 1989 is in our view far too long, particularly when it was prompted by a complaint from a member of the public.*

10.4.2 *We also comment in passing on the need to keep contemporaneous medical records, so that at the very least, those who care for the patient afterwards know what steps have been taken.*

11.0. POLICE INVOLVEMENT 7 JUNE 1989

11.1.1 During the afternoon of 7 June 1989 the Police from Notting Hill Police Station, Ladbroke Grove, London W10, were called to Manor Court Chambers because the various families who were resident there did not want to move out. Christopher Clunis was one of the persons who did not want to move out. There was, according to police records, something of a demonstration and they stayed for a while to ensure there was no breach of the peace. No mention appears to have been made about the attack by Christopher Clunis on the staff during the previous evening.

11.1.2 Later, during the evening of 7 June 1989, the Notting Hill Police were called again to Manor Court Chambers because Christopher Clunis would not leave his room. They went up to Christopher Clunis' room but could not gain access. Suddenly he rushed out at the officers, grasping a table knife, which 3 policemen had to wrestle from his hand. He was removed to a place of safety under S 136 Mental Health Act 1983. Dr Leigh was contacted at St Charles' Hospital and he was then assessed by a Mental Health Team. A detention Order under S 2 Mental Health Act 1983 was made and he was taken to the Henry Maudsley Ward, St Mary's Hospital, Praed Street, Paddington, London W2 at 1 am on 8 June 1989. He was noted to be dishevelled, unkempt, avoiding eye contact, plucking aimlessly at his beard, malodorous, unresponsive and with possible auditory hallucinations. The impression was that he was suffering a relapse of paranoid schizophrenia. He was given a bath, steps were taken to find out some of his history and he was transferred to St Charles' Hospital on 9 June 1989.

11.2. COMMENT

11.2.1 *Christopher Clunis was not charged with any offence despite the fact that he had committed a potentially very serious offence. It seems to be an example of a quite proper desire to divert the mentally ill from the Criminal Justice system, but was inappropriate in the circumstances. In our view detention under S 136 Mental Health Act 1983 was correct in order to deal with the immediate danger, but no thought seems subsequently to have been given as to whether to charge him. This is an example of an occasion when Christopher Clunis used serious violence but was not charged or convicted of any offence. The understandable desire to help him and perhaps not to stigmatise him was allowed to interfere with the process of law, which in our view was ultimately to Christopher Clunis' disadvantage. Since there was no conviction, the event tended thereafter to be brushed aside or trivialised as a minor incident.*

12.0. ST CHARLES' AND HORTON HOSPITALS

12.1. ST CHARLES' HOSPITAL - 9 JUNE 1989 TO 6 JULY 1989

12.1.1. Christopher Clunis was transferred from St Mary's Hospital to the Norland Ward, the Psychiatric Unit, at St Charles' Hospital, Exmoor Street, London W10 on 9 June 1989. While he was an inpatient he was under the care of Dr Anna Higgitt,

Consultant Psychiatrist, Dr Michael Roth, Clinical Assistant to Dr Higgitt and latterly Dr Kluvitse, also Clinical Assistant to Dr Higgitt. We have heard evidence from Dr Higgitt and Dr Roth, both of whom impressed us as to their care and concern for their patient.

12.1.2. During the first few days of admission Christopher Clunis was noted to be clearly deluded, paranoid and threatening to staff. On 13 June 1989 he was prescribed depot injection of Clopixol by Dr Leigh who noted prophetically: "Will pose a placement problem - nursing staff to contact social worker as soon as possible." The nurses noted that he was aggressive and verbally hostile, rude and abusive. His behaviour was noted to be upsetting to other patients, particularly female patients.

12.1.3. Contact was made with Dulwich North Hospital and Dr Higgitt actually spoke to Dr Davies at Dulwich North about Christopher Clunis. She had been Senior Registrar at Dulwich North Hospital so there was good liaison between the two hospitals. Elizabeth Sean Thomas, Psychiatric Social Worker at St Charles' Hospital, also contacted William Horder at Dulwich North, who gave her information about Christopher Clunis' stay at that Hospital. She also contacted Lambeth Social Services. Others from the psychiatric social work team at St Charles' Hospital helped him with financial assistance at certain times.

12.1.4. Christopher Clunis' symptoms continued and Dr Higgitt noted on 30 June 1989: "He is responding to treatment but I know he relapsed fast after 6 weeks treatment at Dulwich North and feel that a longer period of treatment might well be beneficial. More prolonged treatment and possible hostel placement might be better for him. Section 3 would be needed to ensure sufficient treatment."

12.1.5. Dr Higgitt signed a S 3 Mental Health Act 1983 recommendation on that day. Before it could be completed a series of violent incidents took place.

12.2. INCIDENTS OF VIOLENCE

12.2.1. On 2 July 1989 an argument developed between Christopher Clunis and another patient in the dining room of Norland Ward. Christopher Clunis then grabbed a knife from the table and threatened to stab the other patient in the genital area. He was prevented by the prompt action of nursing staff. The police were not involved.

12.2.2. On 3 July 1989 Christopher Clunis stabbed the same patient 5 times late at night while the patient was in his bed. Fortunately the nursing staff were able to intervene and the patient suffered only superficial wounds. The nursing staff considered that they could no longer guarantee the safety of their patients and were concerned for their own safety. On 4 July 1989 they therefore took the unusual step of writing a letter to Dr Roth asking for Christopher Clunis to be transferred to a more secure setting. It was decided that he should only have access to plastic cutlery. The Police were again not involved.

12.2.3. Dr Roth agreed with that assessment and it was decided that he needed more secure accommodation than that which St Charles' could provide. Contact was made with Horton Hospital but no bed was available there. His medication was increased and he was given Special Nursing, which means that he was nursed on a 1 to 1 basis.

12.2.4. A further medical recommendation under S 3 Mental Health Act 1983 was made on 4 July 1989 by Dr Seth of St Mary's Hospital, and the Approved Social Worker, Elizabeth Thomas made the Application on the same day. He was detained at St Charles Hospital under S 3 Mental Health Act on 4 July 1989. In fact a bed then became available at Horton Hospital and he was transferred there on 6 July 1989.

12.3. HORTON HOSPITAL - 6 JULY 1989 TO 27 JULY 1989

12.3.1. Christopher Clunis was transferred to the Derby Unit (the Intensive Care Unit) at Horton Hospital, a General Psychiatric Hospital at Epsom, Surrey during the afternoon of 6 July 1989 under the care of Dr John Wilkins, Consultant Psychiatrist. The Derby Unit was a locked ward providing beds for the Riverside Mental Health Unit, including St Mary's and St Charles' Hospitals. We have heard evidence from Dr Wilkins and he told us that he trained as a forensic psychiatrist.

12.3.2. On admission Christopher Clunis was found to be unco-operative. He was evasive and argumentative and abusive to both staff and patients. He threatened to stab a fellow patient. However he improved on medication but continued to have delusions and lack of insight . On 19 July he was noted to be "likely to become aggressive under pressure" and on the following day was said to be "unpredictable". He was transferred back to St Charles' Hospital on 27 July 1989 and a transfer summary was written by Dr Milne, Registrar to Dr Wilkins. We were told by Dr Wilkins that the nursing staff from St Charles' visited Christopher Clunis at Horton Hospital before he was transferred to their care, to make their own assessment.

12.4. ST CHARLES' HOSPITAL - 27 JULY 1989 TO 14 NOVEMBER 1989

12.4.1. Christopher Clunis returned to the Norland Ward at St Charles' Hospital on 27 July 1989. On his return Dr Roth noted that Christopher Clunis was still thought disordered with some paranoid ideas but there was no hostility or aggression. He planned to resume contact with Lambeth Housing Services in respect of Christopher Clunis' discharge plans. Dr Roth thought he should be discharged to a supportive hostel. The nursing staff noted that he spent most of his time in bed and was drowsy. Dr Lambert, Senior Registrar felt that his medication needed to be reduced gradually and that was done. On 2 August 1989 he was transferred to Avondale Ward where he settled well. On 10 August 1989 some of the nursing staff felt his mental state was deteriorating. On 18 August 1989 he exposed himself in the canteen and on 22 August 1989 he was noted to have some obsessional behaviour and to be rude to black female staff. The nursing staff noted that he could be aggressive if they were not diplomatic with him. He continued to behave inappropriately with female patients and it was felt that his mental state needed close monitoring.

12.4.2. On 4 September Dr Roth discussed Christopher Clunis with Hugh Murray. He was told that Lambeth Housing Services were prepared to accept responsibility for housing Christopher Clunis and that Rosemead Hostel was the only available hostel in Lambeth with psychiatric supervision. Hugh Murray said he would visit Christopher Clunis regularly in order to make a proper assessment for that Hostel.

12.4.3. At the beginning of September 1989 Dr Kluvitse noted that Christopher Clunis still had obsessional symptoms and was still neglecting himself. Occupational Therapy was organised. At the end of September 1989 Dr Higgitt described him as well and feeling that his current medication suited him.

12.5. INCIDENTS OF VIOLENCE

12.5.1. On 29 September 1989 Christopher Clunis hit a woman patient round the face after she had pulled his chair away. A further incident with the same patient took place 2 days later when he punched her in the left eye after some minor provocation. On 10 October 1989 he had a quarrel with another patient when they hit one another. He then returned to the ward with a knife which, on request, he gave to the nurse saying that he was going to stab the patient in the eye" once he had put on his sand shoes". The other patient had apparently threatened to stab him.

12.6. DISCHARGE

12.6.1. He was due to go to see Rosemead Hostel on 6 October 1989 but that appointment was cancelled as were two other appointments. He went to see Rosemead on 25 October 1989 and had an assessment there on 31 October 1989. He was offered a place at the Hostel. Over the next few days he was noted to be behaving inappropriately and he was particularly offensive to a domestic worker. He was discharged from St Charles' on 14 November 1989 and was given an outpatient appointment for 11 December 1989. He did not keep it.

12.6.2. An undated discharge summary was written by Dr Kluvitse in which the diagnosis was given as paranoid schizophrenia, and reference was made to his history of violence and aggression, and to his medication.

12.7. COMMENT

12.7.1. *We consider that it was unsatisfactory that no bed was available for Christopher Clunis in a locked ward when he was seriously disturbed and violent, and when there were real fears for the safety of other patients and staff. This is an example of a lack of resources, which we came across on several occasions during the course of the Inquiry. Fortunately a bed was found after 2 days; but in the meantime Christopher Clunis had been placed on increased medication and we have the impression that the bed was probably made available at the expense of another patient's welfare.*

12.7.2. *Dr Higgitt's team at St Charles Hospital devoted a great deal of time and effort to Christopher Clunis' care and treatment and in our opinion probably did more to help him than any other hospital. However, we are concerned that Christopher Clunis was discharged into the community at a time when he was still demonstrating signs of disturbed and disinhibited behaviour. This again may have been prompted by pressure on beds. Despite the worrying signs, no formal S 117 Mental Health Act 1983 plan was made, although appropriate accommodation had been arranged and an out patient appointment was given. St Charles' Hospital did not notify South Western Hospital about Christopher Clunis moving to their area because they were unsure whether the placement at Rosemead would last and they intended to follow him up for the next 3 months. That information does not seem to have been effectively transmitted to the staff at Rosemead. Dr Roth told us that during the week before Christopher Clunis was discharged he asked the local*

Community Psychiatric Nursing Department to organise Christopher Clunis' prescription for regular depot injections. However he made no record of so doing and the first record we can find about Christopher Clunis in the Tooting Bec Hospital Community Psychiatric Nursing Department notes was made on 1 December 1989, some 2 weeks after his discharge from St Charles'. Dr Higgitt told us that the policies and procedures for S 117 plans were not put in place until about 1990, after the Royal College of Psychiatrists had advised on S 117 procedure. We comment in passing that the Act had come into force some 7 years earlier. That was a serious shortcoming in the care provided for Christopher Clunis as was the fact, as we find, that no proper arrangement had been made for Christopher Clunis to receive his depot injections.

12.3.3. Dr Roth accepted that Christopher Clunis had tried to stab people on a number of occasions but told us, "I noticed that through all of the threats of violence and waving knives there were just four abrasions to a hand recorded as actual injury. And I regarded Christopher Clunis, at that time, as somebody who made a lot of threats with knives and was probably not a dangerous person." We accept Dr Roth's integrity but consider his views were misguided. In our view the effects of the attacks were only limited because of timely intervention by others. We feel there is a real danger of looking too much at the consequences of an action without looking at the action itself. Threatening a police officer with a knife which it took 3 officers to wrestle from him, threatening a fellow patient in the genital area with a knife, and equipping himself with a knife in order to stab someone in the eye are all, in our view, serious episodes which should not be brushed aside because no serious damage was done. We feel that Dr Roth's view was given with the best interests of his patient at heart, but we feel his view was misguided and such a superficial view can ultimately lead to serious danger to the patient or to the public or both.

12.3.4. Again we must emphasise that Dr Roth was not alone in minimizing Christopher Clunis' violence. It is a feature that we have come across time and again during our investigations and we express our concern that such a gloss was in the end detrimental to Christopher Clunis' best interests.

13.0. ROSEMEAD HOSTEL

13.0.1. Rosemead Hostel is situated at 126 Atkins Road, Balham, London SW12. It is a rehabilitation residential hostel, offering short to medium term residence, and run by Lambeth Social Services to rehabilitate young psychotic men who have suffered from psychiatric illness. The residents, in theory, come under the care of the Consultant Psychiatrists at the South Western Hospital. We were told that it is a highly structured rehabilitation hostel.

13.0.2. Christopher Clunis began to live at Rosemead Hostel on 14 November 1989. Unfortunately we have not been able to hear evidence from any of the workers at Rosemead who were there during the time Christopher Clunis was a resident, since none of them are still working there. We have however seen the records kept by the Hostel.

13.0.3. Christopher Clunis' sister told us that she and her children used to visit him at Rosemead.

13.1. APPLICATION TO LIVE AT ROSEMEAD

13.1.1. An application for Christopher Clunis to live at Rosemead was made while he was still an in patient at St Charles' Hospital. A Social Worker at the Hospital should have prepared a report to support the application but the social worker was ill. Dr Roth took on the task in the interests of his patient of preparing a social work report in order that there should be no delay in the application and his prospective place should not be lost.

13.1.2. We were impressed by Dr Roth's obvious care of Christopher Clunis and accepted what Hugh Murray told us about Dr Roth. Hugh Murray felt that Dr Roth had established a very good relationship with Christopher Clunis, not least because he re-awakened his interest in music, tried to obtain sheet music for him and to obtain finance for an instrument. Finding someone to be his friend was all too rare an occurrence for Christopher Clunis, and at that time he seems to have been helped beyond the call of their professional duty by both Dr Roth and Hugh Murray. The social report was done in a hurry and as Dr Roth pointed out, he is not a social worker. It was written for one specific purpose. However it is ironic that the contents of that report were handed from hospital to hospital and relied on and somehow gained a value all of their own.

13.1.3. An Initial Assessment Form of Christopher Clunis was completed by a Supervisor at Rosemead, namely Angela Earle, on 31 October 1989 in which she recorded that there were no risk factors of violence or aggression. We do not know how she came to make that statement; it seems very likely that she relied on what Christopher Clunis told her himself. She identified Dr Roth (Clinical Assistant to Dr Higgitt at St Charles' Hospital) as the doctor with whom he would need regular appointments and stated that he required medication. The copy of her assessment was sent to Dr Kluvitse (also Clinical Assistant to Dr Higgitt at St Charles' Hospital).

13.1.4. An application to live at Rosemead was then completed by a Social Worker, Kathryn Hobson, as well as by Christopher Clunis and also by Dr Kluvitse. It is noteworthy that in that part of the assessment form completed by the social worker, the name and address of Christopher Clunis' sister and her telephone number was given and reference was made to a S 117 Mental Health Act 1983 conference being held to arrange his future support and plans. It is also noteworthy that Dr Kluvitse did not mention any history of violence or aggression or any risk thereof in the form.

13.1.5. A further form was filled in when Christopher Clunis began to live at Rosemead. That form also noted his sister's name, address and telephone number and named his Consultant Psychiatrist as Dr Atakan at South Western Hospital. We point out that such a statement was contrary to the previous information given to Rosemead and contrary to the decision by St Charles' to continue caring for him for some 3 months after his discharge. We do not know how this error occurred.

13.1.6. The discharge summary from St Charles' Hospital was sent to Dr Simon Shepherd, General Practitioner and Medical Officer to Rosemead Hostel. The summary stated, as mentioned above, that Christopher Clunis' diagnosis was paranoid schizophrenia and referred to his history of violence and aggression and to his medication including depot injection to be given every three weeks. It did not refer to the fact that he had been given a follow up appointment at St Charles' for 11 December 1989, nor was he told that St Charles' Hospital was going to follow him up for the next 3 months. We have heard evidence from Dr Shepherd and we found him an impressive and thoughtful witness. We were told by Dr Higgitt that the summary was given to the staff at Rosemead, although it was not in the records which were sent to us. However the summary was sent to Hugh Murray.

13.2. NOVEMBER 1989 TO FEBRUARY 1990

13.2.1. On arrival at Rosemead it was noted that Christopher Clunis had been given a depot injection that morning and would need a further injection on 5 December 1989. Christopher Clunis was seen by Dr Shepherd's partner, Dr Sally Ryder, on 15 November 1989, the day after his admission. She had clearly seen the discharge summary and took a history from Christopher Clunis. He was seen the following day by Dr Shepherd who gave him a medical certificate for 3 months so that he could obtain benefits. A week later Dr Shepherd saw him again for a chat and to get to know his patient.

13.2.2. As no arrangement had been made by St Charles' Hospital for Christopher Clunis to be given further depot injections, on 27 November 1989 his Resettlement Officer, Hugh Murray, referred him to the Community Psychiatric Nursing Department at Tooting Bec Hospital. Still no arrangement was made for the injection to be administered and so on 5 December 1989 (the date the next depot injection was due), Hugh Murray contacted Dr Roth at St Charles' Hospital and arranged for a prescription to be sent by facsimile from Dr Roth to the Community Psychiatric Nursing Service. As a result, Mr John Doherty, Community Psychiatric Nurse, called at Rosemead on 7 December 1989 and gave Christopher Clunis his depot injection. We consider that only timely intervention by Christopher Clunis' Resettlement Officer, Hugh Murray, prompted the regular administration of his medication. Hugh Murray told us that Dr Shepherd had also realised that there was no prescription for Christopher Clunis' depot injection and had taken steps to remedy this deficiency.

13.2.3. Things at Rosemead did not however go smoothly. On 5 December 1989 Christopher Clunis was noted to have been harassing female staff, and he was warned to improve his behaviour or he would be asked to leave Rosemead. At the end of December 1989 he was reported to be staying in bed, leaving rubbish and dirty clothes in his bedroom and his personal hygiene was poor. He was said to be rude and abusive and very demanding of staff. He started to work at the Share Community Scheme on 8 January 1990, a work experience project for people with mental health difficulties run by the West London Community Care Trust. However on 16 January 1990 Christopher Clunis told a woman at the Scheme that the clothes she was wearing were an invitation to rape. He was no longer accepted on the Scheme.

13.2.4. Hugh Murray visited Christopher Clunis regularly at Rosemead and helped him with the problems that had arisen at Rosemead and with more mundane but important matters such as his bus pass and benefits. He helped him to settle down at the Hostel. He told us that all his visits were very structured in that he spoke to the Duty manager for half an hour, then to Christopher Clunis for an hour or more and then spoke to the staff again for a further half hour. He told us he expected full communication between himself and the staff at Rosemead. He attended the first review meeting at Rosemead on 30 January 1990 with Christopher Clunis and was able to help Christopher Clunis understand that some of his behaviour to women was inappropriate and that he needed to improve in certain ways at the hostel.

13.2.5. Hugh Murray told us that he thought Christopher Clunis was quite a clever person who resented some of the demands of the staff at Rosemead and often challenged their requests. That created some excitement and sometimes offence. The staff were concerned that he should accept that his behaviour was wrong but Christopher Clunis did not find it easy to accept that in such terms. Christopher Clunis did not feel that he was ever acting maliciously and therefore felt that people should accept his behaviour. Hugh Murray tried to make him understand that some of that behaviour was anti-social and unacceptable. He also told us that he felt Christopher Clunis was immature, but intelligent and very good in an argument.

13.2.6. Dr Roth visited Christopher Clunis at Rosemead sometime in January 1990. He made no note but has a clear recollection that he visited and stayed for about 1 and a half hours. He went with a psychology trainee who had known Christopher Clunis while he was on the ward. They had a coffee with him. Dr Roth did not recall talking to the staff but from the letter he wrote subsequently to Dr Atakan, it is clear that they told him that he had lost his place in a sheltered workshop because he had made sexist remarks and sexually harassed someone. The staff also told him they were trying to place him in another workshop with some remedial counselling. He did not ask whether he had been to a general practitioner. He thought Christopher Clunis seemed fine and was aware that he was accepting his depot injections. In Dr Roth's view Christopher Clunis was managing well, and therefore it appears that he decided to transfer his care from St Charles' Hospital to Dr Atakan at South Western Hospital.

13.2.7. At the beginning of February 1990 Christopher Clunis tried to gouge a fellow resident's eye, causing him to suffer a swollen and bruised eye, after the latter had made an offensive racial remark.

13.2.8. On 8 February 1990 Dr Roth wrote to Dr Atakan at South Western Hospital introducing Christopher Clunis, telling him of his placement at Rosemead since November 1989, that a Community Psychiatric Nurse was administering the depot injections, and referring to some of the difficulties he had encountered while at Rosemead. He continued: "I feel ... that he should at this time be assessed by his catchment area psychiatric unit so that you are acquainted with him in case of any problems arising in the future." He asked Dr Atakan to send Christopher Clunis an outpatient appointment and enclosed discharge summaries from St Charles', Dulwich North, Chase Farm and Horton hospitals.

13.2.9. South Western Hospital has no record of Christopher Clunis at all. Dr Higgitt told us that before he wrote that letter Dr Roth would have telephoned South Western Hospital to find out who would be caring for Christopher Clunis. Dr Roth received no reply from Dr Atakan but felt that since the hostel was a supportive, supervised hostel they would ensure that he saw a Consultant Psychiatrist. An appointment was apparently made for Christopher Clunis to see Dr Atakan on 22 June 1990. We do not know who made that appointment, but he was never seen and no one ever followed it up. It may be that the staff at Rosemead made that appointment, but we have no way of telling and the South Western Hospital has no record of the appointment at all.

13.3. FEBRUARY 1990 TO OCTOBER 1990

13.3.1. On 26 February 1990 Christopher Clunis began to work for Remploy and his behaviour seems to have become far more acceptable at Rosemead Hostel. When Hugh Murray saw him on 30 March 1990 he appeared to have settled well and was enjoying his work at Remploy.

13.3.2. He had in the meantime been seeing John Doherty, the Community Psychiatric Nurse. We have not heard evidence from John Doherty, but we have seen the full notes that he made. From those notes it is clear that he knew Christopher Clunis' history (although the St Charles' discharge summary from Dr Kluvitse is not with his notes) and planned to visit Christopher Clunis every three weeks, administer the injection and assess his mental state and observe any side effects at each visit. He wrote to Dr Shepherd telling him of this plan. We have not been able to discover from the records who prescribed the depot injections from time to time after Dr Roth's initial prescription. Overall we feel it is likely that it was prescribed by a doctor at Tooting Bec Hospital, London SW17 since it was to Tooting Bec that Dr Roth wrote originally with the prescription and the Community Psychiatric Nurse was attached to Tooting Bec Hospital.

13.3.3. John Doherty visited Christopher Clunis every three weeks and gave him his depot injection on each occasion and kept Dr Shepherd informed. He evaluated Christopher Clunis' problems and needs on 8 February 1990, and again on 2 April 1990; part of the evaluation was to ensure that Christopher Clunis was seen regularly by Dr Shepherd and that his medication was reviewed regularly. We do not think he was successful in ensuring that the medication was reviewed regularly. His view was that Christopher Clunis was generally coping well but that the potential problem of a relapse remained, for which he needed regular monitoring. We point to the excellent follow up when John Doherty attended Rosemead on 2 March 1990 to find that Christopher Clunis was not there but was at work at Remploy. He therefore made an arrangement to see Christopher Clunis at 5 pm on 5 March 1990 at Rosemead, but Christopher Clunis had not returned from work when Mr Doherty attended at that time. He therefore went to see him at Remploy on the following day and administered the injection. We consider this is evidence of good care in the community; but it is of note that such care is time consuming, costly and a drain on resources, although it is effective.

13.3.4. In April 1990 Christopher Clunis' keyworker at Rosemead, Martin Standish, wrote a full report on Christopher Clunis noting both the inappropriate incidents, and the areas where things were going well, and setting out a list of objectives for the future. We consider this was just the sort of help that Christopher Clunis needed.

13.3.5. At the beginning of May 1990 he was noted to be insulting to staff at Rosemead but that did not prevent Martin Standish making a fairly positive report about Christopher Clunis to the Review meeting held on 11 May 1990. The review meeting acknowledged the progress he was making and referred to the areas where he needed to make more improvement. Hugh Murray attended the meeting. John Doherty was not invited to attend the meeting and had he been invited it might have been realised that Christopher Clunis had not seen a Consultant Psychiatrist since January 1990, 4 months previously.

13.3.6. On 15 May 1990 Christopher Clunis did not to go to work at Remploy because of an aggressive incident with a fellow employee the day before. On 19 May 1990 Christopher Clunis was involved in a shouting match with a fellow resident about a television programme. On 28 May 1990 Charlotte Tinker, then his named keyworker, prepared an assessment, referring among other matters to his obsessive behaviour, and setting out a number of objectives in which Christopher Clunis needed encouragement and supervision. One was that he should attend an appointment with Dr Atakan on 22 June 1990. He did not do so and no one appears to have followed this up. By this time he had not been seen by a Consultant Psychiatrist for 6 months. John Doherty was continuing to visit and administer the depot injection throughout this time. He had long talks with Christopher Clunis and felt there was nothing untoward. We are not sure what communication there was between the staff at Rosemead and John Doherty. It may well be that they were each "caring" for him in isolation; and were not pooling their information. Certainly John Doherty was later critical of the fact that two case conferences had been held about Christopher Clunis at Rosemead, neither of which had he been invited to attend.

13.3.7. Hugh Murray visited Christopher Clunis on 29 June 1990 when Christopher Clunis expressed the view that Rosemead was too restrictive.

13.3.8. At the end of June 1990 Christopher Clunis was told by the staff at Rosemead that his behaviour at Rosemead was inappropriate and that he must mend his ways. In July a fellow resident complained that Christopher Clunis had made overt homosexual advances to him, which Christopher Clunis said he had made as a joke. He was told that his discharge from Rosemead would be recommended. He was verbally threatening and insulting to staff and fellow residents.

13.3.9. At Remploy he was warned about his absenteeism, lateness and his attitude to work and this was followed up by a written warning dated 26 June 1990. Neither he nor the staff at Rosemead showed this letter to Hugh Murray. Then, by letter dated 24 July 1990, his employment at Remploy was terminated. The letter stated, "...of particular concern was your belligerent attitude towards your fellow workers and indeed your physical abuse of them. This attitude and behaviour has persisted outside the factory gates with your threatening one of our employees, a circumstance that involved the police." Hugh Murray was not shown that letter either.

13.3.10. John Doherty continued to visit every three weeks and had noted nothing amiss. Indeed on 5 July 1990 he noted, " He continues to attend Remploy which he appears to enjoy... Seems to be mixing quite well with other residents at Rosemead. No evidence of side effects detected from present medication."

13.4. EMERGENCY CASE CONFERENCE 27 JULY 1990

13.4.1. On 23 July 1990 an emergency case conference was called. Hugh Murray was concerned that Rosemead had apparently already decided that Christopher Clunis should no longer live at Rosemead. On 24 July 1990 Hugh Murray had a long talk with Christopher Clunis. The case conference took place on 27 July 1990 at Rosemead Hostel which Hugh Murray (Resettlement Officer) and Michael Bryant (Homeless Single Persons Team Leader), and John Doherty (Community Psychiatric Nurse) also attended. A report was prepared for that conference which referred to the fact that Christopher Clunis was no longer taking his oral medication, although he was receiving his depot injection every 3 weeks. It was thought that his abuse of staff and residents might be related to his mental state. His personal hygiene was poor.

13.4.2. It is clear from the records and what we have been told by Hugh Murray and Michael Bryant, that there was a difference of view about Christopher Clunis at the meeting. The staff at Rosemead felt his behaviour was inappropriate and that he was making little or no attempt to improve. The members of the Homeless Single Persons Team and the Community Psychiatric Nurse acknowledged that he was not easy to deal with, but felt that a strict authoritarian approach was not the best way of encouraging him to change his ways. We have sympathy with both sides. Rosemead decided to discharge Christopher Clunis in 2 weeks time. In the event Rosemead finally agreed not to do so until alternative accommodation had been found for him. This appears to have been agreed only at the direct instigation of Hugh Murray and Michael Bryant, who contacted James Parnell, the Principal Manager of the Adult Residential Care Section of Lambeth Social Services. Mr Parnell apparently directed Rosemead not to discharge Christopher Clunis until a suitable placement had been found for him. We commend Hugh Murray and Michael Bryant for the stance they took. It would have been wholly inappropriate to have discharged Christopher Clunis, who needed supervised care, precipitately into bed and breakfast accommodation or a homeless hostel.

13.4.3. On 14 August 1990 there was an argument between Christopher Clunis and a fellow resident when he struck the other on the head twice with the handle of a walking stick. This cannot have been an easy time for either Christopher Clunis or the staff or residents at Rosemead; it was vital therefore to ensure that he was receiving proper treatment for his illness. However he did not see a Consultant Psychiatrist nor does he seem to have been taking his oral medication.

13.5. CHANGE OF COMMUNITY PSYCHIATRIC NURSE - SEPTEMBER 1990

13.5.1. Then in September 1990 John Doherty left the Community Psychiatric Nursing department. At this crucial stage when Christopher Clunis' care was breaking down (he had already lost his job, and was about to lose his home) his regular contact with John Doherty was also to come to an end. It is unfortunate that John Doherty did not introduce his replacement, Mrs Bala Sivakumar, to Christopher Clunis before he left or take steps to ensure that he was seen by a Consultant Psychiatrist. Hugh Murray was not told that Christopher Clunis was not seeing a Consultant Psychiatrist and he should have been. There was too little communication between the various people who were all trying to care for Christopher Clunis.

13.5.2. Mrs Bala Sivakumar is a Community Psychiatric Nurse attached to the Tooting Bec Community Nursing department. We have heard evidence from Mrs Sivakumar. She felt strongly that there should have been a proper handover by John

Doherty so that she had met Christopher Clunis before treating him. She did recall a short discussion about Christopher Clunis with John Doherty, but told us she had to rely mainly on the notes he had made.

13.5.3. Bala Sivakumar went to Rosemead to give Christopher Clunis his depot injection on 7 September 1990. She was chaperoned by a member of the Rosemead staff since she did not know Christopher Clunis, and that caused him to become upset and aggressive. She was however able to give him his injection. She did not review the case in any way but simply arranged to return 3 weeks later to administer another depot injection. Bala Sivakumar gave us the impression that she considered the staff at Rosemead were responsible for caring for Christopher Clunis and that her role was essentially to administer his injection with little or no liaison with the staff at Rosemead. In our view Christopher Clunis needed real help from all those concerned with his care at this time.

13.5.4. Bala Sivakumar gave Christopher Clunis a further depot injection on 28 September 1990. She told us she found him receptive and pleasant. She had no idea that he was shortly to leave Rosemead. On the basis of her assessment she discussed matters with a member of staff at Rosemead and together they thought that he should be able to attend the Depot Clinic at South Western Hospital. In the actual circumstances where he was doing nothing all day, had lost his job, was shortly to lose his home, had not seen a Consultant for 9 months, was not taking his oral medication, and was continuing to be difficult we find it hard to understand how that decision was reached. In our view he needed more supervision and help, not less. Bala Sivakumar told us she did not know any of this and that it came as a complete surprise to her when she was told on 5 October 1990 that Christopher Clunis had left Rosemead and was now living at Jeffrey's Road. This highlights the failure of communication in that it leads to lack of proper care for the patient. When she asked the staff at Rosemead why he had had to leave she was told he was being overfamiliar and interfering. She did not speak to Hugh Murray about the matter.

13.5.5. On 4 October 1990 Christopher Clunis was discharged from Rosemead Hostel and went to live at Jeffrey's Road Hostel, 33-35 Jeffrey's Road, Clapham, London SW4. He obtained this accommodation through the help of Jenny Norville (Lambeth Housing Special Needs) and Hugh Murray.

13.6. COMMENT

13.6.1. *There is no doubt that Christopher Clunis enjoyed the longest period of stability at Rosemead since he became ill in 1986. As Hugh Murray said to us, Rosemead did a very good job in helping him achieve a position where he could look after himself (with help) and could go to work on a regular basis. He felt that they had not acknowledged their own success. We agree. However it seems to be the case that the staff at Rosemead did not realise that a substantial part of Christopher Clunis' anti-social behaviour was caused by his mental illness. This points to a lack of information and communication from those who were responsible for caring for his health.*

13.6.2. *The picture that emerges is of a number of people all trying to help and care for Christopher Clunis but doing so in isolation from one another. There was little effective communication between those who were caring for him and they each looked after him in the light of their own observations instead of as a team all working together to provide effective care.*

13.6.3. Although St Charles' Hospital had S 117 Mental Health Act 1983 duties, responsibility was never effectively transferred to the South Western Hospital. Furthermore the staff at Rosemead failed to ensure that Christopher Clunis kept his outpatient appointment. There was no proper handover between the Community Psychiatric Nurses. Above all, no one was co-ordinating his psychiatric care and treatment in the community.

14.0. JEFFREY'S ROAD HOSTEL -

14.1. OCTOBER 1990 TO MARCH 1991

14.1.1. We have not been able to speak to any member of staff from Jeffrey's Road Hostel and no records from the hostel relating to Christopher Clunis have been found. This is so despite Hugh Murray having requested that all files relating to Christopher Clunis held by Lambeth Social Services be collected together and preserved after the murder of Jonathan Zito in December 1992. Christopher Clunis' sister told us that she visted him there. Much of our information comes from Jenny Norville's records.

14.1.2. Jeffrey's Road Hostel no longer exists. It was staffed residential accommodation run by Lambeth Social Services. A social worker and an occupational therapist from the Homeless Single Persons Team attended the hostel on a daily basis. Hugh Murray was involved in monitoring Christopher Clunis but others were providing his care. We were told that each resident had his own General Practitioner at Jeffrey's Road, but Dr Shepherd seems to have continued as Christopher Clunis' General Practitioner during the time he lived there.

14.1.3. Bala Sivakumar was due to give Christopher Clunis his injection on 19 October 1990 but she was away on that day; she did not know if she was on holiday or had been ill. The Community Psychiatric Nurse who went in her stead noted, "Seems quite well on immediate presentation. Chatty and quite cheerful". However on 17 October 1990 Christopher Clunis had damaged the door of a fellow resident's bedroom. Nevertheless according to Jenny Norville's notes, he preferred Jeffrey's Road to Rosemead and he was looking after himself better.

14.1.4. Bala Sivakumar gave the next depot injection on 9 November 1990 when she noted that Christopher Clunis was asymptomatic and asked him to attend the Mental Health Clinic for his next injection, to which he agreed. It seems that Bala Sivakumar did not speak at any length to the staff at Jeffrey's Road and she told us she knew nothing of the violent incident that had occurred in October. Perhaps not surprisingly Christopher Clunis did not attend the appointment on 29 November 1990 at the Clinic, so Bala Sivakumar attended Jeffrey's Road with a student nurse to give him his injection. He gave a variety of excuses for not making the appointment, was given the injection and agreed to attend the Clinic for his next injection in December 1990.

14.1.5. On the same day, 29 November 1990, a case Conference was held about Christopher Clunis which Jenny Norville, and Hugh Murray attended. Others may have been present but we have been unable to find out who. It does not appear that

Bala Sivakumar was present. It was thought that Christopher Clunis would be helped by a programme and that he should see a Consultant Psychiatrist as he had not seen one for some time. In fact he had not seen a Consultant Psychiatrist for 10 months.

14.1.6. On 20 December 1990 he failed again to attend the Mental Health Clinic for his depot injection and in Bala Sivakumar's absence a colleague visited him and gave him the injection. The Nurse noted that Christopher Clunis said that the injection was giving him side effects which he did not like, and he felt he needed to see a Consultant Psychiatrist about a change in his medication. However no appointment was made for him. Then Bala Sivakumar and a student nurse visited Christopher Clunis again at Jeffrey's Road on 10 January 1991. He complained about the student nurse being present but accepted the injection. No mention was made about him seeing a Consultant Psychiatrist regarding his medication and it was not raised by Bala Sivakumar, despite the previous note made by her colleague on 20 December 1990.

14.1.7. Between 17 October 1990 and 9 January 1991 Christopher Clunis had been visited regularly by an Occupational Therapist, Miss Saxton. He was frequently in bed when she called (even in the afternoon) and she obviously found him an uphill task. Hugh Murray visited from time to time also. There was a great deal of communication between Miss Saxton and Hugh Murray, because they were part of the same Team and had desks next to one another. Hugh Murray became concerned at Christopher Clunis' lack of motivation and that he was using other residents to carry out chores.

14.1.8. On 4 February 1991 in Bala Sivakumar's further absence, another Community Psychiatric Nurse colleague attended Christopher Clunis at Jeffrey's Road. He again said that he wanted a doctor to review his medication because of side effects, and the Community Psychiatric Nurse made him an appointment to be seen in Dr Atakan's clinic at St Thomas's Hospital on 22 February 1991 at 2 pm. We learned from Dr Oakeley, Consultant Psychiatrist at St Thomas's Hospital, that Dr Atakan held clinics at St Thomas's at that time although she was Consultant Psychiatrist at the South Western Hospital. There is no record of this appointment either at South Western or St Thomas's Hospitals.

14.1.9. Christopher Clunis attended Dr Shepherd's surgery on 5 February 1991 and was given a sick note for 6 months so that he could obtain benefits. However he failed to attend the outpatient appointment at St Thomas's on 22 February 1991. It is of note that by this time Christopher Clunis had not been seen by a Consultant Psychiatrist for 13 months since Dr Roth had visited him at Rosemead.

14.1.10. Both Hugh Murray and Miss Saxton attended a case conference at Jeffrey's Road on 26 February 1991 when it was thought he had settled well but that there was a lack of motivation and that he needed to take active steps to improve himself. No mention was made of his missed appointment at St Thomas's Hospital. Bala Sivakumar did not attend and was probably not invited.

14.2. REFUSAL TO TAKE MEDICATION

14.2.1. Bala Sivakumar called to give Christopher Clunis his injection on 26 February 1991 but he was not there. She left a message and he rang up later that day and told

Bala Sivakumar that he would not have the injection unless he was given an outpatient appointment for his medication to be reviewed. She therefore made an appointment for him at, we believe, South Western Hospital, but the appointment was for 12 April 1991, some 6 weeks hence. She visited Christopher Clunis to give him his injection and to tell him about the appointment but he was very angry, said the appointment was too far away and refused to have the injection. Miss Saxton heard the altercation and informed Hugh Murray.

14.2.2. On the following day, 27 February 1991, Bala Sivakumar contacted Dr Atakan's secretary and left a message for Dr Duignan to call back in Dr Atakan's absence. Dr Duignan called back on Thursday, 28 February 1991 and said that she could not make a domiciliary visit to Christopher Clunis on that day, and asked Bala Sivakumar to discuss the matter with Dr Atakan on her return the following week. Bala Sivakumar left a message at Jeffrey's Road to be passed on to Christopher Clunis.

14.2.3. Bala Sivakumar made no note of her contact with Dr Atakan, but she told us that she spoke to her and that she was told to make the appointment with Dr Oakeley at St Thomas's, because Christopher Clunis was living in the St Thomas's catchment area and had never been seen at the South Western Hospital. On 6 March 1991 Bala Sivakumar made an appointment for Christopher Clunis to be seen in Dr Oakeley's Clinic on 14 March 1991 at 10.30 am. She notified the staff at Jeffrey's Road and asked them to tell Christopher Clunis about the appointment. She told us that she thought it was the responsibility of the staff at Jeffrey's Road to ensure that he attended the outpatient appointment. She also said that she did not contact Christopher Clunis again because he would not have agreed to see her. In the meantime he was without any medication.

14.2.4. Hugh Murray was concerned not least because it was a term of Christopher Clunis contract with Jeffrey's Road Hostel that he should take his medication. He discussed the matter with Bala Sivakumar on 5 March 1991 and said he would try to persuade him to accept the injection. He was not successful, but Christopher Clunis said he would attend his new appointment and would then accept the injection. However Christopher Clunis did not attend Dr Oakley's Clinic on 14 March 1991. Indeed he had been arrested by the Police on 12 March 1991. Bala Sivakumar was not informed of this.

14.2.5. Although Bala Sivakumar remained Christopher Clunis' Community Psychiatric Nurse and responsible for giving him his depot injection, it was not until 2 April 1991 (5 weeks after he had refused medication) that she left a message for Hugh Murray asking him to tell her what had happened. According to her records Hugh Murray did not return her call, so she left a further message on 11 April 1991. She then apparently spoke to Hugh Murray and learned that Christopher Clunis had been evicted from Jeffrey's Road but that he did not know where he was now living. Bala Sivakumar wrote on 15 April 1991 to Dr Shepherd telling him about this. Her letter concluded, "At present there is very little I can do, so I am discharging him."

14.3. COMMENT

14.3.1. *We are concerned that at the beginning of March 1991 the Community Psychiatric Nursing Service, through Bala Sivakumar, did nothing more about a domiciliary visit, did not tell Christopher Clunis about the outpatient appointment that had been arranged, nor take any step to see that he attended the appointment or had the injection which was by then well overdue. Once again the people who were caring for him were doing so, in effect, in isolation and with no overall supervision. That was probably because no one was apparently taking responsibility for his overall care in the community at that time. There was no proper communication between the hostel, social workers and the Community Psychiatric Nurses.*

14.3.2. *We consider that the more disturbed Christopher Clunis became, the less effective care he received; and that is yet another feature which we found repeated over the years. This all points to a failure to have a proper S 117 Mental Health Act 1983 aftercare plan in place which was properly supervised and coordinated.*

15.0. POLICE INVOLVEMENT

15.1. 12 MARCH 1991

15.1.1. On 12 March 1991 the Police were called to Jeffrey's Road Hostel because, as they recorded, Christopher Clunis was chasing the residents round the hostel with a carving knife. We were told by Hugh Murray, and it is recorded in various contemporaneous records, that he in fact chased one fellow resident with a large knife. The resident was locked in the Hostel Office for his own protection. The Police attended and Christopher Clunis was seen to be holding a knife with a 7 inch blade. He swore at the Officer and said he did not want to talk. He would not put it down and then raised it at the Officer. The Officer called for further assistance which arrived and Christopher Clunis then put the knife down. He was arrested for Breach of the Peace and he replied, "I am going to get them all, just wait." He was said by the police to be very violent at the time of arrest. The staff at Jeffrey's Road described him as out of control.

15.1.2. Christopher Clunis was placed in a cell at Clapham Police Station and was not granted bail. Hugh Murray was informed and told the duty Probation Officer that Jeffrey's Road Hostel would not have Christopher Clunis back to live. Hugh Murray informed us that he was surprised at Christopher Clunis' sudden breakdown. He was not referred to Hospital or to a doctor, despite the fact that he was obviously unwell. We were told by Superintendent Barker that, as a result of her Inquiries, an officer at Clapham Police station had told her that he had little confidence in the local Hospitals, and doubted that a Hospital would have detained and or treated Christopher Clunis had they taken him there. She said that despite the seriousness of the offence it was difficult to make out a specific charge, save for assault, because Christopher Clunis had only threatened people and then in a private place. She said that she doubted that a person would be charged with assault unless there was physical contact.

15.1.3. He appeared before South Western Magistrates Court on 13 March 1991 and was bound over for one year in the sum of £500. We should point out that a bind over does not become part of a person's criminal record because it is not deemed to be a conviction. We were told by Superintendent Barker that the victim of the assault was unwilling to prosecute and that may have been the reason why Christopher Clunis was dealt with only for breach of the peace.

15.2. COMMENT

15.2.1. *We are concerned that the Police should consider that no proper charge could be brought. This was a serious offence and the charge of Breach of the Peace does not, in our view, fit the crime. Furthermore it seems to us a matter of real concern that a mental patient's serious crimes are overlooked, often because the victim is not willing to prosecute, probably because he knows the assailant is mentally ill. We agree that it is right to keep the mentally ill away from the Criminal Justice system for minor offences. But it seems wrong to us that a person who is mentally ill should not be prosecuted for committing a serious offence, and should thereby be deprived of the real help which he might otherwise receive under a Hospital Order or via the Probation Services. We consider that the Police should encourage the victim to prosecute in such a case.*

16.0. 74 BABBINGTON ROAD, STREATHAM

16.1. MARCH 1991

16.1.1. Christopher Clunis was placed by Lambeth Housing in bed and breakfast accommodation because all supervised accommodation had now been exhausted. He did not attend the outpatient appointment at St Thomas's on 14 March 1991. Christopher Clunis telephoned Hugh Murray on 14 March 1991 and told him of his new address which was temporary accommodation at 74 Babbington Road, London SW16. Hugh Murray collected Christopher Clunis' valuables from Jeffrey's Road and took them to him at his new address. He had a discussion with Christopher Clunis and told him why he could not go back to Jeffrey's Road. Hugh Murray told us that when he saw him at Babbington Road, Christopher Clunis was not exhibiting any psychotic features, but his concern was that Christopher Clunis was a danger to himself (in that he could not look after himself properly, would not wash or feed himself and would not leave his room) rather than a danger to anyone else. Hugh Murray told Christopher Clunis that he would make further applications for more suitable housing for him. He stayed at that accommodation until 26 March 1991 and then seems to have moved to 70 -74 Augustin Avenue, Croydon but this is by no means certain. At that stage Hugh Murray who worked for Lambeth Social Services lost contact with Christopher Clunis. We have been unable to find out whether he received any treatment or care during the 4 months between March and July 1991.

16.2. COMMENT

16.2.1. *This was exactly what Hugh Murray and Michael Bryant had feared; if Christopher Clunis went to bed and breakfast accommodation and then left, there would be no way of keeping track of him. Hence they had worked hard to keep him at Rosemead until proper alternative accommodation had been sorted out. Giving temporary accommodation to a homeless man does not mean that he will go to the accommodation, let alone stay there, so that there is no effective way of keeping track of such people. Christopher Clunis was therefore lost to Hugh Murray for a period of 4 months and with no care it is perhaps not surprising that he again relapsed and was picked up by the Police.*

17.0. POLICE INVOLVEMENT

17.1. 23 JULY 1991

17.1.1. On 23 July 1991 the Police found Christopher Clunis outside a Co-operative Shop in Brixton Hill, having stolen sweets from inside the store. He was sucking a dummy. He was removed to a place of safety under S 136 Mental Health Act 1983 and was taken to Brixton Police Station where he was assessed. Hugh Murray was informed of his arrest and told the police of his previous psychiatric history.

17.1.2. Under the S 136 procedure agreed between the police and St Thomas's Hospital such a patient is taken to the South Western Hospital for assessment and a bed allocated from there if the patient requires admission. St Thomas's Hospital forms part of the West Lambeth Community Care Trust with the South Western Hospital and Tooting Bec Hospital. Together they provide the full psychiatric unit of the Trust consisting of in-patient and out-patient facilities at each hospital. Christopher Clunis was therefore taken by the police to South Western Hospital, Landor Road, Stockwell, where he was seen and assessed by Dr Ilves. Hugh Murray telephoned Dr Ilves to give him background information. Dr Ilves thought he was suffering from an acute relapse of schizophrenia with a possibility of drug abuse and paranoid ideas. Dr Ilves considered that he needed to be admitted. Under the rota system operated by the Consultants at South Western and St Thomas's Hospitals for patients of no fixed abode, Christopher Clunis was admitted as a voluntary patient under the care of Dr David Roy, Consultant Psychiatrist at South Western Hospital. However as no beds were available at South Western, it was arranged that he would be transferred to St Thomas's Hospital.

17.2. COMMENT

17.2.1. We consider that a S 136 assessment was an entirely appropriate response to the bizarre offence committed by Christopher Clunis at this time. The fact that only a very minor offence had been committed meant that, in our view, it was entirely proper not to charge him but to provide him with access to health care.

18.0. ST THOMAS'S HOSPITAL

18.1. 23 JULY 1991 TO 17 AUGUST 1991

18.1.1. Christopher Clunis was admitted to Lloyd Still Ward, St Thomas's Hospital, Lambeth, London SE1 on 23 July 1991 under the care of Dr Henry Oakeley, Consultant Psychiatrist. We have heard evidence from Dr Oakeley and from Mr Sean Singh Sidhu-Brar (known on the Ward as Sean Singh) who was at the time Staff Nurse in charge of Lloyd Still Ward.

18.1.2. On admission he was seen by the duty psychiatrist to whom he was unwilling to talk. It was felt that he was suffering from schizophrenia, and medication was pre-scribed. On the following day he had a fight with another patient and was intimidat-ing. The clinical note stated that he was not to leave the ward. Subsequently he was aggressive and threatening and the nursing staff requested that he be transferred to the local Intensive Therapy Unit, namely Eden Ward at South Western Hospital. The matter was discussed with Dr Atakan, Consultant Psychiatrist at South Western

Hospital, who advised that he should be contained on the ward on medication. Dr Oakeley suggested to us that it was very likely that this decision was made because Eden Ward was already full so that Christopher Clunis could not be transferred there.

18.1.3. Hugh Murray visited Christopher Clunis on Lloyd Still Ward on 25 July 1991 and noted that he was in a very serious psychotic state. He prepared a report for the Ward on Christopher Clunis' history, gave them the name of his General Practitioner and his last Community Psychiatric Nurse, and gave them the St Charles' discharge summary. Dr Oakeley told us that they had had no difficulty obtaining documents relating to Christopher Clunis' previous hospital admissions and that they had all arrived together and probably from St Charles' Hospital. Hugh Murray visited again the next day and found Christopher Clunis still very unwell. By 31 July 1991 when he attended a Ward, round Hugh Murray found Christopher Clunis more settled and recorded that it was agreed that he was still subject to S 117 Mental Health Act 1983 aftercare on his discharge. Dr Oakley gave evidence to us that in his view Christopher Clunis was always ann informal patient at St Thomas's. We note in passing that Christopher Clunis should still have been subject to S 117 Mental Health Act 1983 aftercare as a result of his discharge from St Charles' and Dulwich North Hospitals. Hugh Murray told us that Dr Oakeley felt that Dr Atakan should take S 117 Mental Health Act 1983 responsibility since she had been responsible formerly and that it was finally agreed that the responsibility should be Dr Roy's at South Western Hospital because the patient had been admitted under him in the first place. A place at Verdant House in Lewisham was discussed as a residence to which Christopher Clunis might be discharged. This was a residence in the private sector to which West Lambeth Health Authority had exclusive access.

18.1.4. On 1 August 1991 Dr Oakeley's Senior House Officer contacted the South Western Hospital to see whether Dr Roy now had a bed available for him, but it appears he did not. In the event Dr Oakeley continued to take responsibility for Christopher Clunis. He told us that once he had returned from holiday on 2 August 1991 he saw Christopher Clunis every day. Further aggressive outbursts occurred on 2 August 1991 when he also punched the Staff Nurse and broke the glass in the dormitory door. Over the following weekend he attacked a fellow patient, pulled the fractured leg of another, and threatened others. His medication had been increased throughout his stay and Dr Oakeley advised a further increase in medication to try and contain his disturbed behaviour. Dr Oakeley told us that he prescribed 500 mgs Chlorpromazine 4 times a day and in addition, as required, 200-400 mgs Chlorpromazine also 4 times a day, making a maximum of 900 mgs Chlorpromazine 4 times a day. He described this as "an extremely large dose." He told us that once or twice a year he will prescribe a patient 400 mgs Chlorpromazine 4 times a day, but only once or twice in his life has he exceeded that dose and he did so with Christopher Clunis. As a result Christopher Clunis was monitored very carefully by Dr Oakeley who told us he saw him every day, sometimes twice a day to ensure there were no side effects.

18.1.5. Sean Singh described the dose as "putting him in a chemical strait jacket." Dr Oakeley disagreed with Sean Singh's opinion and told us that the medication was given for proper treatment and not for containment. Sean Singh told us that he thought that Christopher Clunis was prescribed such a high dose in order to contain him on an open ward because no bed was available on the locked Eden Ward at South Western Hospital. Dr Oakeley disagreed and said that he would have treated Christopher Clunis no differently had been under his care in a locked ward. Sean Singh also told us that there were only about 6 beds on Eden Ward and that it was very difficult, if not impossible, to place a patient there as a preventive measure, particularly from St Thomas's Hospital, since it was not 'on site'. Dr Oakeley denied this. Sean Singh was a full time Psychiatric Nurse for 10 years and worked part time for 7 years thereafter. He doubted the therapeutic value of the high level medication given to Christopher Clunis save as a containment measure where alternative hospital care was not available.

18.1.6. Despite such high doses, Christopher Clunis remained threatening and intimidating and there were no side effects. On 7 August 1991 he had a tooth extracted which was carried out under general anaesthetic because of his unpredictable behaviour. Thereafter he remained unpredictable and aggressive, and on the evening of 7 August said " if you give me any more of that stuff [medication] I will beat you up." However from about 10 August 1991 he appeared calmer. Then on 14 August 1991 he attempted to kick another patient and to burn another with a cigarette. On 15 August 1991 he was still aggressive and intimidating and a nurse noted that his "mental state is nowhere near 100% to normality". On 17 August 1991 he was agitated and threatened the nursing staff and said he was going to get his mates to stab them. He and his belongings were then found to be missing from the ward, just after midday on 17 August 1991. The Police were informed. We were told by Sean Singh that a bed was kept open for him. This did not mean his bed was left unoccupied because there is such pressure on beds, but Christopher Clunis' name was written up on a board in the Ward so that, if he returned, he could occupy a bed vacated by someone on leave or be admitted as an urgent case, if necessary by sending another patient on leave. However he did not return. On 21 August 1991 when Christopher Clunis had not returned to the ward Dr Oakeley advised that other local hospitals and the police should be informed. He was formally discharged form the hospital in his absence on 23 August 1991.

18.1.7. Dr Oakeley considered that Christopher Clunis was at all times willing to be an informal patient and there was no indication that he wanted to leave the ward or was unwilling to take his medication. He accepted that it might have been apparent that Christopher Clunis intended to leave the ward shortly before he did so, but that he had never given any indication of so doing previously. He told us that had Christopher Clunis ever refused medication or indicated he was intending to leave the Hospital he would have been detained under the Mental Health Act 1983. He felt strongly that as long as a patient was willing to stay and be treated on the ward voluntarily it was best not to subject the patient to compulsory detention. We respect that principle, but given the degree of violence shown by Christopher Clunis on the ward, his threat to beat up the staff if he were given more medication, and the very high dose of Chlorpromazine he was on, we consider that he should have been detained under S 3 Mental Health Act 1983 for the safety of himself and others.

18.1.8. Hugh Murray felt that Christopher Clunis was initially content to be an informal patient, but that if it had become clear that there was a serious risk of his walking out of the Hospital he should have been detained under S 5(4) Mental Health Act 1983. The staff felt he had not improved appreciably, and Hugh Murray thought he was still psychotic and not ready for discharge. He was not told that Christopher Clunis had left the Hospital until two days after the event. Hugh Murray felt that was indicative of the lack of concern shown by the Hospital staff. He felt real concern for the general public if Christopher Clunis was at large and was behaving as he had done on the ward, and he made it clear to the nursing staff that he wanted to be told if any information came to light as to Christopher Clunis' whereabouts.

18.1.9. On 27 August 1991 the Psychiatric Nurse, Mr Steven Taylor, at Spur House Resettlement Unit telephoned Sean Singh on Lloyd Still Ward at St Thomas's Hospital, after Christopher Clunis had attacked another resident. He made a note of the telephone conversation. Steven Taylor told Sean Singh that Christopher Clunis was resident at Spur House and asked for details of his medication, which he was given. No mention of this telephone call was made in the nursing records at Lloyd Still Ward by Sean Singh, and Dr Oakeley said he was not informed. Indeed, when this information was imparted to him by the Inquiry, he was astonished that he had not been informed in the light of the fact that he was very keen to readmit Christopher Clunis. Sean Singh could not recall the telephone conversation at all but he accepted that it must have taken place. He thought that, as was his custom when someone from outside the Hospital telephoned about a patient, he would have discussed the patient's mental state, his time and behaviour on the ward and would have said that he had left the ward without permission, that he was under the care of Dr Oakeley and that he was wanted back on the ward. However he would also have said that he had, by then, been discharged from St Thomas's. He felt he would have been bound to have given this history before going into details of the patient's medication. He said that he always documented such telephone calls in a book held on the ward called a "Communication Book". He had tried to find the relevant book but without success. He told us that he was always very thorough about note taking and indeed it is clear from the nursing records that Sean Singh did make full notes in respect of Christopher Clunis while he was on the ward. Sean Singh felt sure that he would have told Steven Taylor that Christopher Clunis was wanted back on the ward, but he was not so sure that he passed on the information about Christopher Clunis' whereabouts to Dr Oakeley.

18.1.10. We were troubled by these differing accounts. It is clear there was a telephone call in which Sean Singh told Steven Taylor details of Christopher Clunis' medication. We have come to the view that Sean Singh probably did not tell Steven Taylor that Christopher Clunis was wanted back on the ward because (i) Steven Taylor would have no doubt jumped at the chance of transferring a difficult resident (who had attacked a fellow resident) to Hospital; (ii) even more so since Christopher Clunis was discharged from Spur House on the following day because of his unacceptable behaviour and Steven Taylor knew of that, since he rang the nurse at the new hostel (to which Christopher Clunis was transferred) to give him details of his medication; (iii) we find it very difficult to accept Sean Singh's assertion that he may not have told Dr Oakeley that Christopher Clunis' whereabouts were now known. The only explanation we can suggest for what appears to be this uncharacteristic failure by Sean Singh is that since Christopher Clunis had by then been discharged, he did not say anything about him being wanted back on the ward.

18.1.11. On 28 August 1991 Dr Pathare, Senior House Officer to Dr Oakeley prepared a discharge summary which he sent to Dr Shepherd's surgery, Dr Shepherd having been his General Practitioner while he was at Rosemead and Jeffrey's Road Hostels. The discharge summary suggested that Christopher Clunis had been allowed weekend leave from which he had not returned. We do not know how that came to be written since it is clear from the contemporaneous records and the evidence that we have heard that Christopher Clunis simply disappeared off the ward and was not fit to be allowed out. Dr Oakeley said that part of the discharge summary was wrong and he was critical of Dr Pathare for making no mention of Christopher Clunis' violent behaviour on the ward. We are troubled by the lack of accuracy in this summary.

18.2. COMMENT

18.2.1. *We consider that it was unsatisfactory that no bed was available for Christopher Clunis in the locked Eden Ward at the South Western Hospital, when he was seriously disturbed and violent, and there were real fears for the safety of other patients and staff. This is another example of lack of resources, similar to that already identified by us in relation to Horton Hospital. We have the impression that, at least partly as a result of the lack of a bed, Christopher Clunis was placed on exceedingly high doses of medication. In our view Christopher Clunis should not have been nursed on a general psychiatric ward when he was so disturbed.*

18.2.2. *We are of the view that Christopher Clunis should have been detained under S 3 Mental Health Act 1983 and on a locked ward during the time he was at St Thomas's Hospital. His level of disturbance should have given rise to anxiety that he might leave Lloyd Still ward and his threat to beat up the staff if they gave him more medication was not, in our view, taken properly into account.*

18.2.3. *We find that Sean Singh did not provide full information about Christopher Clunis to those who came to care for him afterwards. We are of the view that communication of such information is vital to ensure the effective care of a patient.*

19.0. SPUR HOUSE RESETTLEMENT UNIT

19.1. 17 AUGUST 1991 TO 27 AUGUST 1991

19.1.1. The Resettlement Agency is an arm of the Department of Social Security and it exists to house single homeless people. The Agency has Units all over the country but there are five in London. The Units are in the process of being closed down or transferred to the independent sector, but the new system is not yet fully in place. The Units are of varying size but only one in London takes women. Four of the London Units employ a Nurse, but Spur House Unit at the time when Christopher Clunis lived there had two nurses who were employed by the Local Health Authority and attended at Spur House 7 days a week. The Units run a system whereby if a resident behaves violently a Notice, called a Resettlement Unit Information Notice (R.U.I.N.), is sent to the Head Office in Nottingham and is then distributed amongst the Units to alert them to potential problems. Such Notices are issued, in particular, when there is an incident involving serious or potentially serious violence. The Units are used to dealing with minor incidents of violence and skirmishes between residents; they are used to residents being belligerent or irritable especially as the accommodation provided is very much cheek by jowl. The Units have to take a dispassionate view because if a person is refused entry to a Resettlement Unit then he will have nowhere else to go, except on the streets. Obviously the view taken has to take into account the safety of workers at the Unit and that of other residents.

19.1.2. Spur House Resettlement Unit at 12A Ennisdale Road, Lewisham, London SE13 had the capacity to sleep 150 homeless men at that time. Since November 1990 Mrs Elizabeth Bee has been the Manager of Spur House and we heard evidence from her. We also heard evidence from Dr Nargis Begum, who is a General Practitioner in practice with Dr Hussein who was the Visiting Medical Officer to Spur House. We also heard evidence from Mr Steven Taylor, who was a Psychiatric Nurse at Spur House. He told us that approximately 30% of residents "have some kind of psychiatric problem."

19.1.3. We visited Spur House at the beginning of February 1994. Although it is a modern, purpose built unit, the design comprising dormitory accomodation is in our view ill-adapted for the care of mentally disordered people and the poor standard of upkeep and cleanliness we found very disappointing.

19.1.4. Christopher Clunis came to Spur House on Saturday, 17 August 1991 at 7.30pm off the street straight from St Thomas's Hospital having left that Hospital of his own volition. He was interviewed by Mr Lovelock on Monday 19 August 1991. Christopher Clunis said he had been in St Thomas's Hospital for two to three weeks and gave the name and address of his Social Worker, Mr Hugh Murray. Mr Metcalfe was Mr Lovelock's supervisor and on 20 August 1991 he tried to telephone Mr Murray but was unable to contact him. Hugh Murray never received a message to telephone Mr Lovelock. The number Mr Lovelock rang was the Town Hall at Lambeth and it appears that not all calls that are made to the Town Hall get through to the person for whom they are intended. We fully accept that Hugh Murray did not receive the telephone message, since he wished to re-establish contact with Christopher Clunis and was very concerned about him. We accept Hugh Murray's evidence on that point.

19.1.5. Mrs Bee told us that she would have expected one of the Nurses to contact St Thomas's Hospital to find out Christopher Clunis' history. Dr Begum, the acting Visiting Medical Officer, saw Christopher Clunis on a regular twice weekly visit to Spur House on 23 August 1991. She was asked to see him to provide a DSS Certificate so that he could claim benefits. He told her he had an old fracture of his right ankle, and that he was suffering some abdominal pain. She noted he was a schizophrenic which she thought she had been told by a nurse at Spur House. She gave him a Certificate for 4 weeks and that was the extent of her involvement. She did not think about the matter further. She did not contact St Thomas's Hospital to find out about his psychiatric history because she thought the Mental Health Team for Single Homeless People would be dealing with his psychiatric problems at the behest of the nurses at Spur House. She did not think that she had informed Mrs Bee or any of the workers at Spur House of what she had been told.

19.1.6. On 27 August 1991 Mr Metcalfe referred Christopher Clunis to Steven Taylor, the Psychiatric Nurse at Spur House, because he thought Christopher Clunis was in obvious need of psychiatric assessment and was behaving increasingly strangely. Before Steven Taylor was able to see him, Christopher Clunis attacked a fellow resident causing him facial lacerations which required hospital treatment. Steven Taylor rang St Thomas's and spoke to the Staff Nurse, Sean Singh, who informed him of the medication that Christopher Clunis had been prescribed. He noted that the doses were extremely high. According to Steven Taylor, Sean Singh did not tell him that Christopher Clunis had gone absent without leave from St Thomas's or that they were trying to trace him nor did he disclose anything else about Christopher Clunis' history. Stephen Taylor told us had he done so, "I would have made arrangements to get this chap back into hospital." We have already referred above to Sean Singh's recollection of that telephone call and our findings in relation thereto. Suffice it to say here that we accept Steven Taylor's evidence. Such a finding is strongly supported by the evidence of Dr Elizabeth Parker, Consultant Psychiatrist at Hither Green Hospital and at the Mental Health Advice Centre, 1 Southbrook Road, Lewisham, London SE12, from whom we have heard evidence. She held an out patient clinic at Spur House for half a day each month.

19.1.7. Steven Taylor asked her to see Christopher Clunis. She saw him on 28 August 1991 but could not elicit any psychotic symptoms. She prescribed medication for him, on the basis of what she was told by Steven Taylor. She told us that in the normal course of events she would have written both to the Visiting Medical officer to Spur House and to the Hospital from where he had just been discharged, St Thomas's. She could not actually recall the matter but felt that she did not follow Christopher Clunis up in her normal way because she was told that he was moving on. She felt strongly that had Steven Taylor been aware that St Thomas's Hospital wanted Christopher Clunis back on their ward he would have told her. She also told us that had Steven Taylor been told that Christopher Clunis was wanted back at St Thomas's he would have been sent back at once. She told us that it is normally exactly the opposite problem that arises: hospitals do not want the patient back, so the Units are left to cope as best they can. The strong impression we have is that Spur House would have been delighted to be relieved of a problem resident had there been any indication that St Thomas's wanted him back.

19.1.8. The victim of the assault did not wish to bring charges. Once again a serious assault went unnoticed by the Police or the Criminal Justice system. Dr Parker was of the view that the incident had occurred because Christopher Clunis was not receiving his medication. Mrs Bee decided that in view of the serious attack on a fellow resident Christopher Clunis should no longer be allowed to reside at Spur House and would be barred from living at Spur House for one year. However she arranged for him to go to live at another Resettlement Unit, Lancelot Andrewes House, and she did not issue a R.U.I.N. because she felt the attack had been precipitated by the fact that Christopher Clunis had been without his medication. She knew nothing of his history. Mrs Bee thought she arranged the transfer with the Manager of Lancelot Andrewes House, Mr Ivor de Coverly, but he had no recollection of that. Certainly Steven Taylor telephoned the Nurse at Lancelot Andrewes House and gave him details of Christopher Clunis' medication. Spur House provided him with the money for his bus ticket to Lancelot Andrewes House.

19.2. COMMENT

19.2.1. *In our view Spur House was a totally inappropriate place to care for someone like Christopher Clunis with a severe mental illness. It does not have the proper resources to provide adequate care.*

19.2.2. *We did not feel that the Dr Begum, Locum Visiting Medical Officer, made sufficient investigation of the case. At the very least she should have made enquiry about his psychiatric history or prompted others to do so. However set against the background that the residents are generally transient and itinerant we understand why it is such a thankless task to make efforts to find out a man's history only to find that he then leaves with no forwarding address.*

20.0. LANCELOT ANDREWES HOUSE RESETTLEMENT UNIT

20.1. 28 AUGUST 1991 TO 5 MAY 1992

20.1.1. Lancelot Andrewes House is a Resettlement Unit at 96 Great Guildford Street, London SE1, which is able to take 72 homeless men. It runs at something like 95% capacity throughout the year. Some men stay only for a night, some for many months. We heard evidence from Mr Ivor de Coverly, the Manager of the Unit from Mr Ferard George Mr John Taylor Mr Barry Wilton and Mr John Lamb who were all Resettlement Service Officers (now Support Managers) at the Unit; from Dr Adrian McLachlan, the Visiting Medical Officer to the Unit; and from Mr David Purse, Community Psychiatric Nurse with the Three Boroughs Mental Health Team for Single Homeless People.

20.1.2. We were told that the unit has dormitory accommodation. Some dormitories have 20 beds, and one has only 2. It is a very old building, and with men of different backgrounds, low tolerance levels and confined living space "it is a recipe for violence." John Lamb said that there were quite often incidents of violence and fights, and that one had to take a pragmatic approach. Incidents involving weapons, or which caused serious injury or damage, or attacks on officers, were matters about which there would be concern and which would prompt a R.U.I.N. Ivor de Coverly told us that they have a nucleus of about 30 residents but otherwise the residents are transient, and "several thousands of people, I would say, on an annual basis come through our doors." He described alcohol and drug abuse as major problems and increasingly, he said, there is a "problem of people who are mentally unstable." He said they were ill equipped to deal with the mentally unstable. He said he thought lack of information about a resident was the most serious problem, which made running the Unit very difficult and that this lack of information resulted from the issue of confidentiality. He said that the Citizens' Charter was also very difficult to operate in these circumstances. He said that had he known of Christopher Clunis' violent history he would not have permitted him to reside at the unit. However he told us that if they pointed him in the direction of another hostel they would not disclose his violent history, because that would jeopardise his place. Therefore the whole cycle could be repeated yet again.

20.1.3. Barry Wilton told us that the Unit was the last resort for people whom nobody wanted. There is nothing for such people after the Unit, "There's just the streets, I'm afraid." John Lamb told us that the Units do not and cannot provide full care for an individual, particularly if that person suffers from mental illness.

20.2. ARRIVAL AT LANCELOT ANDREWES HOUSE - 28 AUGUST 1991

20.2.1. Christopher Clunis was admitted as a resident to Lancelot Andrewes House on 28 August 1991. On the following day he was interviewed and gave a considerable history, some of which was correct but some of which has never been verified. He told them of his admissions to Chase Farm and St Thomas's Hospitals. He would not give the name of his social worker as he said he wanted to make a fresh start. Spur House was contacted and disclosed that he had attacked another resident and had previously been in a psychiatric ward at St Thomas's. Chase Farm was contacted and they said he had been a patient there and advised the Unit to write if further information was required.

20.2.2. Ivor de Coverly told us that quite frequently new residents did not want to disclose their past but that over a period of time, and as their confidence and trust was gained, further information would be disclosed. However if the resident is adamant that he does not want the Unit to obtain any information they will respect that unless, as in this case, the resident had previously been with another Resettlement Agency Unit. He told us that the Unit provides a home for the homeless but the aim is to try and obtain long term accommodation for the resident and the Unit helps residents with that. He explained the R.U.I.N. system and said it worked well, although recognised that it was of litttle use if a resident used different names.

20.3. SEPTEMBER 1991 TO DECEMBER 1991

20.3.1. On 20 September 1991 Christopher Clunis agreed that Mr Deley, a worker at the Unit, should contact Jeffrey's Road Hostel, which he did. He was told that Christopher Clunis had threatened another resident there and had been discharged. He was also told that he had been in St Thomas's but had left there and that social services had lost touch with him. Mr Deley was given the name of Hugh Murray, Social Worker, and eventually made contact with him on 23 September 1991. Hugh Murray told us that he rang back on the very day he received the message from Mr Deley. He was transferred to the nurse at Lancelot Andrewes House, Mr Rambarran, and read him the report which he had prepared for St Thomas's. He gave the nurse full information about Christopher Clunis' history, including the incident at Jeffrey's Road and the fact that his last hospital admission had been at St Thomas's. The nurse asked for a copy of the report which Hugh Murray had read out and he said he would send it if a written request was made. The nurse told Hugh Murray that Christopher Clunis did not wish to return to the Lambeth area. Hugh Murray heard no more. However Christopher Clunis would not allow the Nurse at the Unit to contact the Hospitals where he had been treated previously, although Mr Rambarran did write to St Charles' Hospital on 24 September 1991 and was sent by Dr Higgitt, 2 days later, copies of a letter to Dr Atakan at South Western Hospital, a discharge summary and a social report.

20.3.2. Dr McLachlan, Visiting Medical Officer to Lancelot Andrewes House told us that he first saw Christopher Clunis on 30 August 1991. The nurse, who was a temporary nurse in Mr Rambarran's absence, took a history and had already received details of his medication from Steven Taylor at Spur House. Christopher Clunis told Dr McLachlan that his illness was due to abusing drugs. Dr McLachlan prescribed medication for him. Some time afterwards, as referred to above, Mr Rambarran received the discharge summary from St Thomas' Hospital and previous hospital records. Dr McLachlan told us that Mr Rambarran was good at obtaining records, "he was good at his job". Although Dr McLachlan was told originally by Christopher Clunis that his schizophrenia was drug induced, he told us that once he had read Christopher Clunis' history he considered he was suffering from a schizophrenic illness with frequent episodes of relapse. He discussed this with Mr Rambarran. Dr McLachlan saw Christopher Clunis from time to time when he complained of back pain for which he prescribed treatment.

20.3.3. Dr McLachlan and Mr Rambarran clearly knew of his diagnosis and of his previous episodes of disturbed and violent behaviour, but it was not their practice to relay this information to the manager or care staff at the Unit because of breaching confidentiality. Dr McLachlan felt that at the times when he saw Christopher Clunis he was not threatening or violent. Neither he nor Mr Rambarran at any time told the other staff during his stay at Lancelot Andrewes House of his history of violence. Dr McLachlan said that with hindsight he should have conveyed this information, as it was something they should have known. He said it was a difficult issue, unless the client consented to the information being passed to others. However he told us that in the Unit in which he presently works there is a much closer working relationship between medical and other staff so that there is much more pooling of information.

20.3.4. Dr McLachlan told us that he did not think the Mental Health Team for Single Homeless People had ever been in touch with him or Mr Rambarran about Christopher Clunis, so that when David Purse of that Team saw Christopher Clunis at Lancelot Andrewes House on 12 December 1991, he would have known nothing of his history.

20.4. PROBLEMS AT LANCELOT ANDREWES HOUSE

20.4.1. On 23 October 1991 Christopher Clunis punched another resident in the face causing considerable facial injury to that resident. John Lamb said that he would speak to Christopher Clunis about the incident but there is no record that he did so. He could not recall the particular incident but he could recall that Christopher Clunis had been involved in fights from time to time, where he either gave or received minor injury. John Lamb wondered whether the other resident had left the hostel and that, he told us, would explain why there was no follow up. There were problems during November 1991 with Christopher Clunis being lazy, and very untidy. Ferard George told us that his untidiness and laziness were "big problems". John Taylor told us his clothes and bedlinen were often dirty and he would do nothing about it even when reminded. Barry Wilton told us that he did not look after his bedspace at all and was always taking food to his bed. He also told us that Christopher Clunis used to stay in bed fully dressed all day. However John Lamb told us that in the scheme of things at Lancelot Andrewes House that was not a major problem. He would not be overly concerned by that sort of behaviour as he took an objective, rather dispassionate view in the interests of the residents as a whole. He had the impression that Christopher Clunis was on medication which was making him rather slow and lethargic, but he felt it was better that he was like that and easier to manage, than that he was active and volatile. He did not think it was warranted for him to spend time and energy trying to persuade Christopher Clunis to get up and tidy his bed.

20.4.2. A worker at the Unit (who cannot now be identified) was concerned about Christopher Clunis on 15 November 1991 and felt he should be considered for a "potentially violent" marking. Ivor de Coverly did not agree. Meanwhile Christopher Clunis was helped by staff at the Unit to find more permanent accommodation.

20.5. INVOLVEMENT OF THE MENTAL HEALTH TEAM

20.5.1. Mr Deley was clearly concerned about Christopher Clunis and asked David Purse, from the Mental Health Team, to see him in December 1991. David Purse saw Christopher Clunis on 12 December 1991. According to David Purse Mr Deley told him that Christopher Clunis had a past history of mental ill health. However Christopher Clunis only told David Purse that he had a long history of drug abuse and was on medication because of that. He said that he had no psychiatric history and did not want any help, save with housing. David Purse did not contact the Dr McLachlan, or Mr Rambarran, or any of the Hospitals where Christopher Clunis had previously been treated to verify this information. He told us about this interview. He accepted Christopher Clunis' assertion that he had no previous psychiatric history, despite what he had been told by Mr Deley. He said: "He certainly didn't give me any cause for concern with his mental health state." He told us that he would only have contacted the Hospitals where he had previously been treated if Christopher Clunis had given his written permission to his so doing. He said he can only provide help if the person is willing to accept it.

20.5.2. On 11 February 1992 Christopher Clunis asked to see David Purse. On 12 March 1992 the Mental Health Team telephoned Lancelot Andrewes House. The note made of the telephone call was: "As client's problems seem to be as a result of drug abuse and as his problems are not mental health problems they are unable to help." David Purse told us that the note reflected his professional judgment although he had offered to help if necessary. John Lamb told us that when he read the report on Christopher Clunis he was amazed, since he thought it was quite obvious that Christopher Clunis was mentally unwell. David Purse repeated to us that he could only go on the information he was given, and that he found Christopher Clunis to be a "gentle giant" who therefore did not warrant further enquiry. He accepted that if he was worried about a man's violence he would impart this information to others without the client agreeing thereto.

20.6. FURTHER PROBLEMS IN THE SPRING OF 1992

20.6.1. In the early part of 1992 Christopher Clunis continued to keep his bedspace untidy and to stay in bed for most of the time. On 13 March 1992, the day after the Mental Health Team's negative response, Mr Deley noted that Christopher Clunis would not give his cooperation to their obtaining medical and other reports. He told Christopher Clunis that this lack of cooperation would prevent the Unit or the Joint Assessment and Resettlement Team helping him with obtaining further accommodation, and he referred the matter to the Welfare Officer, John Lamb. Further efforts to help him find accommodation were made in April 1992.

20.6.2. On the night of 3/4 May 1992 Christopher Clunis walked around his dormitory all night and then set fire to a Bible. John Taylor was extremely worried about him and considered that he was unstable and needed proper supervision elsewhere. He felt he should not be at the Unit any longer. John Taylor told us that he had noticed a change in Christopher Clunis' attitude, from someone who had stayed in bed for 18 to 20 hours a day to someone who was walking around all the time. It concerned him and hence he wrote a full note expressing his anxiety. He told us that he had noticed this change of mood over the previous day or so. He also made a note in the Incident Report Book. Barry Wilton also noticed that although Christopher Clunis was generally inactive he did go through phases when he was irritable, difficult and overactive. John Lamb told us that he had received reports of Christopher Clunis acting in a very odd way, chanting and going round in a circle and then standing still and staring at a person. John Lamb interviewed Christopher Clunis on 4 May 1992, (Bank Holiday Monday), and he told John Lamb he could not sleep because he had not had his medication. His answers were glib and John Lamb was concerned about him and agreed that he appeared unstable. He felt that violence was brewing, but he did not feel so strongly that something had to be done immediately and he bore in mind that during the time Christopher Clunis had been a resident he had not been noted as a violent man. Generally he was described as lazy. Christopher Clunis said he was willing to see Dr McLachlan the next morning so that John Lamb felt that was soon enough, and an arrangement was made for him to do so. He felt that Christopher Clunis needed a specialist psychiatric assessment but he did not intend to call on the Mental Health Team again.

20.6.3. On the night of 4/5 May 1992 Christopher Clunis attacked another resident in the dormitory with a knife. They had apparently been quarrelling earlier in the evening and Ferard George and Barry Wilton had gone down to tell them to be quiet. Barry Wilton told us that Christopher Clunis "wasn't with it" that evening and that he kept denying things, even denying that he was shouting, although he was shouting loudly. Ferard George told us that the victim came into the office with blood pouring down his neck, saying " he stabbed me, you can throw him out now." Ferard George said the victim had been referring to Christopher Clunis. Barry Wilton's recollection was that the victim had come into the office with blood pouring out of his shoulder and said that Christopher Clunis had stabbed him.

20.6.4. The ambulance and police arrived, the victim was taken to Guy's Hospital and Christopher Clunis was arrested. The police spoke to Ferard George and Barry Wilton who took them down to where Christopher Clunis was in the dormitory. The knife was found by the side of his bed. The Police only took a statement from Ferard George, although Barry Wilton was also a witness to the incident. Subsequently Ferard George was told of the date of trial, 17 August 1992, and was told the Police would be in touch if they needed him to attend. They never were in touch with Mr George to say whether he needed to go to Court, and he never heard from the Police about the outcome of the case. He was particularly annoyed because he had arranged to go on holiday in August, and he did not go in case the police contacted him. The Police did not tell Lancelot Andrewes House the outcome of the case and no member of staff whom we interviewed could recall the Police ever coming to the Unit again regarding the incident. In particular the police did not inquire as to the whereabouts of the victim.

20.6.5. Ferard George was sure that the victim returned to the hostel after he had been discharged from Guy's Hospital. Ivor de Coverly looked up the victim's records for us, and discovered that the victim had returned to Lancelot Andrewes House on 5 May 1992 and left on 12 May 1992. Barry Wilton recalled that the victim had returned to the hostel because he remembered the victim bragging that he had been given 100 stitches. He discounted the suggestion that the victim had been given 100 stitches because Barry Wilton had only seen one wound; he felt the victim was exaggerating to get attention. He remembered the victim was something of a nuisance and he thought that he had been asked to leave. Dr McLachlan recalled seeing the victim after he was discharged from hospital. He thought there had been some cervical nerve injury.

20.6.6. John Taylor told us that Christopher Clunis was a very difficult resident. He referred us to the Incident Report book where it was noted," Every time we move someone next to Mr Clunis they want to move or leave."

20.6.7. John Lamb told us his view of Christopher Clunis following the incident on 4 May 1992, "Of all the people who have been through my hands, I had regarded the fact that he had finally shown that he was a potential killer, that he would kill at random and without provocation". He told us he was astounded to hear that Christopher Clunis had been released after this attack.

20.7. COMMENT

20.7.1. *It is a matter of concern that the information that had been obtained by Dr McLachlan and Mr Rambarran was not passed on to those who were trying to care for him. It seems to us that Ivor de Coverly and John Lamb were trying to walk a tightrope, on the one hand trying to maintain the safety and well being of their staff and other residents, and on the other not forcing a resident out on to the streets. However, they would have been greatly helped in walking that tightrope if they had known Christopher Clunis' full history and there had been a sharing of information between the professionals, and if further follow up had been carried out. We were much impressed by the difficult nature of the job carried out by workers at the Resettlement Units, most of whom have no training whatsoever. They clearly must rely to a great extent on the professional carers with whom they work to help them in assessing and dealing with residents. It seemed to us that there was a real lack of communication. We consider that it is vital that information learned at a Resettlement Unit should be passed on to the people who are actually caring for the resident.*

20.7.2. *We do not consider that the care provided by the Mental Health Team, through David Purse, was satisfactory. Proper enquiries and investigations should have been carried out and a formal assessment by a psychiatrist should have been made. Perhaps the case was not given proper consideration because the referral had come from one of the care workers at the Unit. In our view that should make the Mental Health Team more alert, not less, since laymen were clearly concerned at the resident's mental state. This episode again highlights the lack of communication between those who were supposed to be together caring for Christopher Clunis. We also consider that the staff at Lancelot Andrewes House were let down by the Mental Health Team; we feel that they were entitled to expect more from that Team than was in fact offered.*

20.7.3. *Dr McLachlan told us that things were much better nowadays and that there is good communication within the Three Boroughs [of West Lambeth, North Southwark and Lewisham] Primary Health Care Team for Single Homeless People who are providing primary care for the Single Homeless. We are very pleased to hear it.*

20.7.4. Between July 1987 and May 1992, Christopher Clunis had been an inpatient at no less than four major London psychiatric units: Chase Farm Hospital, Dulwich North Hospital, St Charles' Hospital, and St Thomas's Hospital. Each had lost contact with him.

[NOTE. As Dr McLachlan was abroad when we sent him details of our criticism we were unable to take his response thereto into account.]

21.0. POLICE INVOLVEMENT

21.1 ARREST AND CHARGE MAY 1992

21.1.1. Christopher Clunis was arrested at 2.00am on 5 May 1992 in respect of the stabbing of a fellow resident at Lancelot Andrewes House. He was taken t Southwark Police Station, 323 Borough High Street, London, SE1. We have seen the police records in relation to his arrest and we have heard evidence from Detective Chief Inspector David Wood, Detective Constable Gwynfor Owen and Police Constable Alan Anstead, who are all besed at Southwark Police Station.

21.1.2. PC Anstead arrested Christopher Clunis and DC Owen was the Officer in charge of the case. PC Anstead told us that he had been a Police Officer for over 20 years. He had arrested Christopher Clunis and made a statement, but the matter was then handed over to DC Owen. At Southwark Police Station Christopher Clunis' clothing was taken from him and he was issued with some other clothes; a white suit. The knife was also kept by the Police. He was charged with wounding with intent to cause grievous bodily harm, contrary to S 18 Offences Against the Person Act 1861. When he was charged he replied "That's fine". The charge was a very serious one and it is clear that the Police considered the matter one of considerable gravity.

21.1.3. DC Owen told us he had been in the police force for 12 years and a detective Constable for 3 years. He recalled the case from the records he had seen, and from memory. When he came on duty on the morning of 5 May 1992 he was told that Christopher Clunis was in the cells and appeared mentally ill. He went to see Christopher Clunis. He told us, "I went down to the cells to have a look at him, and he had spread excrement all over the cell walls and all over himself, so he was obviously not in a fit state to be interviewed." He did not interview him but charged him later that day at 10.55am. We have seen a copy of the Custody Record. There is no mention in the Custody Record that Christopher Clunis had covered himself and the cell in excrement. The Custody record is detailed, and some 20 entries are made between 2.10am on 5 May 1992, when Christopher Clunis arrived at the Police Station, and 10.55 am on 5 May 1992, when he was charged with the offence. DCI Wood told us that "If the cell was covered in excrement it should have been recorded on the custody record." Furthermore we find it odd that he was given a white suit if he really had covered himself and the cell in excrement. It is also wholly out of character; not once in all the records we have perused relating to Christopher Clunis was such a suggestion made. It may be that DC Owen has muddled up this case with another, and we do not accept what he told us on this point.

21.1.4. DC Owen recorded in the Custody Record that Christopher Clunis suffered from mental illness and was not safe with a knife. He was observed closely while in the cell, and he was assessed by a doctor and an Approved Social Worker from Guy's Hospital. DC Owen told us that in his view Christopher Clunis was "very, very dangerous." A Solicitor was contacted by the Police who said he would speak to Christopher Clunis at Tower Bridge Magistrates' Court where he was taken by the Police at 11.41 on 5 May 1992.

21.2. STATEMENTS OBTAINED FOR THE PROSECUTION

21.2.1. Statements were made by PC Anstead and his colleague PC David Hill who had both attended the incident at Lancelot Andrewes House. They both described seeing the victim with who was bleeding excessively from a neck wound. They saw Christopher Clunis in his room and noticed that the pillow and sheet on one of the beds was bloodstained. He was asked if he had just stabbed someone and he replied, "I wish I'd killed him, the knife is under the bed, shall I get it for you?" Later when he was shown the knife with blood on, that had been found by the side of his bed, he denied that it was the knife he had used. He then said he had stabbed the victim with "a human knife".

21.2.2. The victim made a statement in which he said that he and Christopher Clunis shared a room at the Hostel, that he had been concerned that Christopher Clunis was mentally ill and dangerous and had voiced his concerns to the staff at the Hostel. He said that on 4 May 1992 Christopher Clunis had been behaving very oddly, pacing up and down, standing at the end of the victim's bed and staring, and then in the early evening he had begun to shout and swear. The victim informed the staff who asked Christopher Clunis to be quiet. The victim then went to bed but Christopher Clunis kept shouting at him. The victim turned towards the wall away from Christopher Clunis and suddenly felt a sharp blow to his left shoulder. Christopher Clunis then shouted at him "Do you want some more?" The victim saw that he was holding a knife with a 3 inch blade. He said Christopher Clunis was the only person in the room. The victim said he was scared for his life and ran from the room. He was bleeding from his shoulder and he was taken to Guy's Hospital where he was treated.

21.2.3. The victim's statement was dated 5 May 1992 and was signed by him. It included the following words, "I am willing for the police to have access to my medical records regarding this assault." We were told by DC Owen that the statement was taken from the victim at Guy's Hospital by DC Johnson.

21.2.4. Ferard George (member of staff at Lancelot Andrewes House) made a statement to the Police. He described how the victim had, earlier that night, complained about Christopher Clunis' shouting and in response thereto Ferard George and another member of Staff had gone down to the room to tell them both to be quiet. He stated that about half an hour later the victim had come into the staff room with blood coming from his left shoulder and the victim said, "Call the police, he's stabbed me." He rendered first aid to the victim, and the police and ambulance were called. No statement was taken from the other member of staff, Barry Wilton.

21.3. ROLE OF THE CROWN PROSECUTION SERVICE - 5 MEMORANDA

21.3.1 The statements obtained by the Police were passed to the Crown Prosecution Service. We have received written evidence from Mr H.A Youngerwood, Assistant Chief Crown Prosecutor of the Crown Prosecution Service. He told us that between 12 May 1992 and 28 July 1992, five memoranda were sent to the Crime Support

Group at Southwark Police Station asking for medical evidence to be obtained in respect of the victim.

21.4. RESPONSE TO THE MEMORANDA

21.4.1. DC Owen told us he could not recall receiving any of the memoranda. Both he and DCI Wood told us that there was now no record at the Police Station of the memoranda having been received or dealt with. However DC Owen said that he must have received the memoranda and would have acted thereon. He could not however recall what he did. We have asked Mr Youngerwood whether there were ever any replies to the memoranda that were sent by the Crown Prosecution Service and he has told us there were none, save for a telephone message on 10 August 1992 from the Crime Support Group at Southwark Police Station in which they said they were chasing up the last memorandum.

21.4.2. DCI Wood told us that in May 1992, memoranda and replies thereto were not kept by the Crime Support Group at the Police Station. At that time a Diary was kept by a clerk who was allotted to the case. In the case of Christopher Clunis the clerk was called Maureen, but DCI Wood had been unable to find the working Diary she kept for that period of time. He told us she would have entered the memoranda and the replies thereto in the Diary. He also told us that the Detective Sergeant within the Crime Support Group supervises Detective Constables, and he should be the long stop to ensure that, for example a situation does not arise where 5 memoranda remain unanswered. He also made the point that if none of the memoranda was answered it seemed to him very odd that the Crown Prosecution Service had not taken the matter further and spoken to the Detective Sergeant in the Crime Support Group. He told us that generally there is good communication between the Detective Sergeant and the CPS.

21.5. MEDICAL EVIDENCE RELATING TO THE VICTIM

21.5.1. PC Anstead told us it was his understanding that Guy's Hospital always wanted a special form filled in by the victim before they would release the victim's records to the police, and he told us that there is a form, called Form 172, which is kept at the police station for that purpose. We have seen a copy of the form. It is a form produced by the Metropolitan Police for authority to disclose a person's medical condition and treatment. It is not a form specifically required by Guy's Hospital but it is clearly acceptable to them.

21.5.2. DC Owen thought that the victim needed to sign Form 172 despite his signed statement which gave consent to his records being disclosed to the Police. He said this was the procedure he had been asked to follow at Southwark, although he told us it was markedly different from the procedure he formerly adopted when he was at Whitechapel Police Station. At that Police station all that was required was a telephone call to the London Hospital and a report would be prepared. No consent at all from the victim was necessary, he told us, for the London Hospital.

21.5.3. We have heard evidence from Ms Christine Seacole, Medical Records Manager at Guy's Hospital and from Mr Martin Packer, Site Services Manager for Guy's and St Thomas's Hospital. They told us that no special form was or is required by Guy's Hospital. All that was and is required is a signed consent to disclosure from the patient. Both Christine Seacole and Martin Packer told us they had never seen a special form, either from the Metropolitan Police or from Guy's Hospital. Christine Seacole said that to her knowledge the Police had never asked the department about the forms necessary for disclosure of records, nor had they ever asked her at any time since May 1992 for the records held by Guy's in respect of the victim of Christopher Clunis' attack.

21.5.4. DC Owen told us he could not remember whether he had asked Guy's Hospital for medical evidence in respect of the victim, but he felt it was reasonable to assume he had done so. However he felt that Guy's would not have accepted the signed statement of the victim as authority to disclose his medical records. He could not however recall speaking to anyone at Guy's about what they require in order to release records. He had on numerous other occasions in other cases left a signed form at Guy's Hospital in order to obtain a report and had also written to the Hospital sending a form and asking them to prepare a report. As the Officer in Charge of the case he would have seen that a statement had been taken from the victim and would have realised that Form 172 had not been signed. He could not recall why he had not asked an officer to have one signed while the victim was still in hospital. He said that the victim gave a false name to Guy's Hospital but he could not recall how or when he learned that.

21.5.5. DC Owen then said that Guy's, "would need some sort of authority. The problem is with this one is that ...we couldn't send that statement to the hospital. It's got a different name on it, to their records." He told us that from memory there was a problem with the victim's name and the Hospital tracing his details.

21.5.6. We find it very difficult to establish what happened about the medical evidence in respect of the victim. If we accept that DC Owen thought that Form 172 needed to be signed by the victim and that the victim's statement would not, on its own, be sufficient for the Hospital to release the records, then since the victim could not be traced, we cannot see how a request would ever have been made of the Hospital. However he told us that a request had been made.

21.5.7. Alternatively if DC Owen thought, despite what he told us, that the signed statement of the victim was sufficient authority, then since, as he told us, the victim had given a false name, one wonders how the signed consent would have helped. The Hospital either would not have been able to trace any records for the victim, or if they did, they would not have disclosed them because the consent was not in the same name as the records. We are concerned that DC Owen may have only learnt that the victim had been known at Guy's Hospital under a different name as a result of the investigations carried out by our Inquiry. We heard evidence from him some considerable time after we had learned that the victim was known by a different name at Guy's Hospital. Certainly there is no reference in the police records to the fact that the Police knew he had given an assumed name to Guy's Hospital. We have not been able to take the matter further with him.

21.5.8. We were told that Guy's Hospital keep records of all requests made for patients' notes and have done for many years. We were told, "we do keep very strict records." It was only with their help that we were able to track down the victim's notes and it was only as a result of these investigations that it was discovered that the victim was known by a different name at the Hospital from the name known to the Police. They however had no record of a request between 5 May and 17 August 1992 either in the name of the victim known by the Police, or in the name known by Guy's, which differed only by one syllable. It seems to us that the name Guy's recorded was likely to have been a result of mis-hearing rather than a deliberate attempt to give a false name. The victim was known by his real name at Lancelot Andrewes House, and by the Police, and by the Police National Computer; it seems to us very unlikely that he gave a false name. He certainly gave his correct Christian name. We can understand how in the early hours of the morning the mistake could have arisen. We do not consider that the slight alteration in name could explain the lack of medical evidence in respect of the victim.

21.5.9. The final piece of information which we have been able to obtain is in relation to the victim's injuries. Guy's Hospital disclosed the medical records to us. They show that he had suffered a stab wound in the left side of his neck which was associated with pain on breathing and pain with shoulder movement. He was given a full examination and a 2 cm wound posterior to the clavicle was sutured. The stitches were to remain for 10 days. He was admitted in the early hours of 5 May 1992 to Guy's Hospital for observation but was discharged later that day. The injury did not turn out therefore to be serious, although we take the view that it could have penetrated an artery or severed nerves, and was therefore potentially serious. As we understand it the Police never learned the extent of the victim's injury.

21.6. ATTEMPTS TO TRACE THE VICTIM

21.6.1. DC Owen told us that he tried to find the victim. He went to Lancelot Andrewes House at some time, although he did not know the date, but the victim had left. We have been able to find out, as referred to above, that the victim remained at Lancelot Andrewes House until 12 May 1992. DC Owen then made an enquiry on the Police National Computer and circulated the victim's name on the Computer so that if the Police came across him they would contact DC Owen. Again he could not recall when he had done that because he had no note. However on 4 June 1992 DC Owen was notified that the victim was staying at St Mungo's, 88 Endell Street London WC1. He made a note thereof. However by the time DC Owen went to see him he had gone. PC Anstead told us that he had made no attempt to find the victim after he had gone missing.

21.6.2. DC Owen was sure that the Crown Prosecution Service knew the victim could not be traced long before the case came to Court. He said, "They were fully aware by that time otherwise they would have called upon myself to go to Court as well." He told us no police officer had gone to Court, "Because CPS knew for a fact that [the victim] couldn't be traced and that is why they called the case up to come to court to discontinue it." He told us that had no decision been made before going to Court, he would have been asked to attend Court as the Officer in Charge of the case. He was adamant that the CPS knew before the matter went to court on 17 August 1992 that the victim could not be traced. PC Anstead told us that he attended Court on 17 August 1992.

21.6.3. DCI Wood told us that Southwark Police Station deals with something like 17,000 crimes a year and offences of wounding and wounding with intent with knives, glasses and even guns are not that uncommon. To a great extent they have to rely on the victim being willing to assist in the prosecution. He said that since the victim in this case was clearly not interested in assisting the Police it might have been a case which fell through the net. It seemed to us that he was troubled, as are we, that where the Defendant was thought by the Police to be very, very dangerous, thorough steps should be taken and properly recorded to ensure that society is safeguarded.

COMMENT

We found DC Owen an unimpressive witness whose bearing and demeanour gave little cause to persuade us to accept his evidence. We are sorry to record our finding that we do not accept the greater part of his evidence. It seemed to us improbable that diligent efforts were ever made to obtain medical evidence or to trace the victim. We are concerned that DC Owen may not have investigated the matter in the way his training would require, perhpas because the attack had been perpetrated by someone who was mentally ill on a person who was homeless. When he had assessed Christopher Clunis as very, very dangerous, it seems to us that more effort, not less, should have been spent in ensuring that the case could be properly prosecuted.

22.0. FORENSIC SERVICES FOR SOUTH EAST LONDON

22.1. HMP BELMARSH

22.1.1. HMP Belmarsh is a prison at Thamesmead, London SE28 and was opened in about 1990. We heard evidence form Dr Percy Brown who is the Managing Medical Officer at the prison who is responsible for all the health requirements of the prisoners and staff. We also heard from Dr Janet Parrott, Consultant Forensic Psychiatrist who runs the Bracton Clinic (a Medium Secure Unit) in Bexley, Kent and is the Visiting Consultant Forensic Psychiatrist to HMP Belmarsh. A team of psychiatrists of Senior Registrar status operates each day at the Prison under her supervision. A team supervision meeting is held once a week on a Tuesday at the Prison attended by Dr Parrott, the Managing Medical Officer and the Psychiatric Senior Registrar, when cases of particular difficulty are discussed.

22.1.2. Dr Parrott has headed the team which runs the psychiatric service at the Prison since about May 1991. The service provided is that every new prisoner is seen at, or shortly after, admission both by a medical officer and by a health care worker. Any prisoner who has a psychiatric history or who is seen to have a psychiatric problem is admitted immediately to the health care centre within the prison, where he is cared for according to an assessment of his dangerousness to himself or others. All new cases are seen and assessed by the psychiatric medical officer either on the day of admission or the next day. Dr Brown spoke eloquently in praise of the scheme which he says provides prisoners with a proper psychiatric service which is lacking at many other prisons. We thoroughly commend the scheme. Ironically, it appears that at HMP Belmarsh the prison population receives better care for their physical ailments than they would if they were at liberty. Dr Brown told us that whereas outside prison there might well be a long waiting list to see an Orthopaedic Surgeon, in HMP Belmarsh a prisoner will be seen within days.

22.2. TOWER BRIDGE MAGISTRATES COURT

22.2.1. A Court Diversion Scheme operates at Tower Bridge Magistrates Court in that a Psychiatrist of Senior Registrar status attends the Court and assesses persons charged with an offence who may have a psychiatric problem. The Court Liaison Psychiatrist is part of a forensic team also headed by Dr Parrott. We thoroughly commend the use of this scheme.

22.3. THE BRACTON CLINIC

22.3.1. The Bracton Clinic is a Regional Medium Secure Unit, situated within the grounds of Bexley Hospital, for mentally ill patients who require a high level of security in the long term. The Unit has 15 beds serving a population of about 850,000 and covers the Lewisham, North Southwark, Greenwich and Bexley areas. 15 beds is the quota allocated under the Butler Report norm whereby it was suggested that 20 beds were needed for every million of the general population. For the whole of the South East Thames Area a total of 90 Medium Secure Unit beds are provided which is 8 more than the Butler norm. However for a number of reasons, including the fact that the Bracton Clinic serves a socially deprived Inner City area, and the fact that it provides a full psychiatric service at HMP Belmarsh, 15 beds have proved to be insufficient at the Bracton Clinic and there have not been sufficient beds in other Units in the Region to take Bracton's overflow. We have heard evidence from Dr Parrott, Consultant Forensic Psychiatrist at the Bracton Clinic, and from Dr Anderson, her Senior Registrar. We have also heard evidence from Mr Anthony Clark, Unit Business Manager for Bexley Community Health.

22.3.2. In general it is considered by the Consultant Team at the Bracton Clinic, and confirmed by the Unit Business Manager, that some 8 - 10 more beds have been and are still needed to cope with the number of patients who should be cared for within a Regional Medium Secure Unit. Because of the lack of beds, as indicated above, it is frequently necessary to place a patient within the private sector. That is undertaken by the General Consultant Psychiatrist who has ultimate responsibility for the patient, not the Consultant Forensic Psychiatrist. The General Consultant Psychiatrist has to find an appropriate bed for the patient at a Private Hospital, and then has to ensure that funding will be forthcoming to pay for that bed. There is no formal requirement for a member of staff from the Bracton Clinic to keep in touch with the patient once he has been transferred to the private sector. Dr Parrott and her team are concerned at this lack of liaison and therefore have established a policy whereby a nurse or doctor occasionally attends the patient at the private hospital so that a link is maintained with the service to whom the patient would eventually be re-transferred. Each case which has been transferred elsewhere is considered at a weekly multi-disciplinary meeting at the Bracton Clinic.

22.4. BEXLEY HOSPITAL

22.4.1. Bexley Hospital is a General Psychiatric Hospital which has an Intensive Care Unit. We were told that the Intensive Care Unit is a locked ward and cares for patients during the acute stage of an illness, so that a patient is expected to be cared for on the Unit for only a matter of one or two weeks before being transferred to an open ward at the Hospital. It is less secure than the Regional Medium Secure Unit.

COMMENT

We approve of the careful selection and review procedures for deciding which patients require to be admitted to a secure unit. However it is abundantly clear that South East London has insufficient beds for the patients who need admission to secure facilities.

This has resulted in placements in the independent, private sector which are dependent on funding from the General Psychiatric Service. The costs of such a placement are high and the need for economy can be an overriding influence so that the time that a patient remains on such a Unit is affected. In addition, placement of a patient in a secure unit in the independent sector interrupts continuity of care and, if the patient is transferred to an independent unit out of the area, may well interfere with potential follow up in his local community.

23.0. HMP BELMARSH

23.1. FROM 5 MAY 1989 TO 29 MAY 1992

23.1.1. On 5 May 1992 Christopher Clunis was taken to Tower Bridge Magistrates' Court by the police. He was remanded to HMP Belmarsh to be returned to Court the following day to see Dr Exworthy, the Court Liaison Psychiatrist.

23.1.2. Christopher Clunis was seen on admission to Belmarsh Prison on 5 May 1992 by Dr Banerjee, Senior Registrar to Dr Parrott, whose impression was that Christopher Clunis was suffering from paranoid psychosis. He arranged for him to be admitted to the Health Care Centre within the Prison, knowing that he was to be seen by Dr Exworthy the next day. Christopher Clunis was seen at HMP Belmarsh by Dr Brown. He told us: "My immediate reaction to Mr Clunis was that he was both of a size and a demeanour to make ordinary people a little bit cautious of him".

23.1.3. On 6th May 1992 Christopher Clunis once again attended Tower Bridge Magistrates' Court where he was seen by Dr Exworthy, also Senior Registrar to Dr Parrott. We have seen a report prepared by Dr Exworthy. He diagnosed that Christopher Clunis was suffering from paranoid schizophrenia and noted that he was aggressive and had hit out at the duty solicitor. Thereafter Christopher Clunis was again remanded to HMP Belmarsh to attend Court on 13 May 1992.

23.1.4. Dr Banerjee saw Christopher Clunis again on 7 May 1992 and was of the impression that he was psychotic and needed to be transferred to a Regional Medium Secure Unit or a locked ward under S 48 Mental Health Act 1983. He discussed the case with Dr Exworthy on the telephone who told him that at Court he had hit the duty solicitor and also tried to hit Dr Exworthy. Dr Exworthy agreed that he needed to be transferred to a Regional Medium Secure Unit under S 48 Mental Health Act 1983. Dr Banerjee spoke to Dr Anderson, Senior Registrar to Dr Parrott at the Bracton Clinic, who said he would discuss the case with Dr Parrott and arrange for Christopher Clunis' urgent admission to the Clinic.

23.1.5. Dr Anderson discussed the case with Dr Parrott and, since no bed was available at the Bracton Clinic for Christopher Clunis, Dr Parrott asked Dr Anderson to discuss the matter with Dr McCarthy (General Consultant Psychiatrist at Guy's Hospital) who was responsible for obtaining an alternative placement for him. He did so and eventually Dr McCarthy was able to persuade the Health Authority to fund such a placement in the private sector.

23.1.6. On 12 May 1992 Dr Banerjee spent a long time trying to discover Christopher Clunis' history. He telephoned the Maudsley Hospital, the Single Homeless Team, the Joint Assessment Resettlement Team, Lancelot Andrewes House, and the Medical Officer to Lancelot Andrewes House. He obtained a very patchy history and details of some hospital admissions.

23.1.7. On 13 May 1992 Christopher Clunis was certified unfit to appear at Tower Bridge Magistrates' Court by Dr Katrina O'Neill - Byrne. She was a Research Fellow in Psychiatry also under Dr Parrott.

23.1.8. On 14 May 1992 Christopher Clunis was seen by Dr Roy, whom we believe was Registrar to Dr Proctor, Consultant Psychiatrist at Bexley Hospital. He noted that Christopher Clunis was schizophrenic and acutely psychotic and in need of treatment at the Regional Medium Secure Unit. He clearly felt that the Intensive Care Unit at Bexley Hospital was not suitable for Christopher Clunis. He discussed the case with Dr Parrott who agreed but said that there was no bed available at the Bracton Clinic and that he was to be placed in the private sector.

23.1.9. On 19 May 1992 efforts were made by Dr O'Neill-Byrne to see whether Christopher Clunis could be transferred to AMI Kneesworth House Hospital. Once a bed had been obtained, authority was given by the Home Office on 28 May 1992 to transfer Christopher Clunis to Bexley Hospital under S 48 and 49 Mental Health Act 1983 and then to Kneesworth Hospital. Christopher Clunis was taken to Bexley Hospital on 29 May 1992 where he was simply checked in before being taken to Kneesworth House on the same day.

23.1.10. We agree with Mr Anthony Clark, the Unit Business manager at bexley Hospital, when he said, "The most appropriate course of action at the beginning of this process would have been for Christopher Clunis to have been admitted to the Bracton [Clinic] if a bed had been available."

24.0. AMI KNEESWORTH HOUSE HOSPITAL

24.1. FROM 29 MAY 1992 TO 17 AUGUST 1992

24.1.1. AMI Kneesworth House Hospital is a private Hospital at Bassingbourne-cum-Kneesworth, Royston in Hertfordshire which provides facilities within the Ashwell Unit similar to those at a Regional Medium Secure Unit.

24.1.2. On 29 May 1992 Christopher Clunis was admitted to the Ashwell Unit under the care of Dr Lomax, Consultant Psychiatrist, who had then been working in forensic psychiatry for about 1 year. Dr Taylor, Consultant Forensic Psychiatrist, worked with Dr Lomax on the Unit. We have heard evidence from Dr Lomax.

24.1.3. On admission Christopher Clunis showed no remorse for the offence, stated that it was a good idea to have stabbed the victim and that he had no regrets. Subsequently he threatened staff and fellow patients and was intimidating in manner although there was a slow improvement in his behaviour over the following weeks. We were told that repeated efforts were made to obtain Christopher Clunis' earlier medical records from hospitals where he had previously been treated, but to no avail.

24.1.4. On 17 July 1992 a report called an Admission Summary was prepared by Dr Lomax in which he diagnosed that Christopher Clunis was suffering from paranoid schizophrenia. On the same day Dr Lomax prepared a report for the Solicitors instructed by Christopher Clunis in relation to the offence of S.18 Offences Against the Person Act 1861 (grievous bodily harm with intent) with which he had been charged. Dr Lomax reiterated the diagnosis, and commented that Christopher Clunis had "readily accepted treatment and there has been some improvement although he is not well enough to leave hospital at this present time." He recommended that an Order be made under S 37 Mental Health Act 1983 (a Hospital Order). He stated in the report that he was willing to attend Court to give additional oral evidence and he told the Solicitor that he would make himself available to attend Court. He told us he would have then been able to tell the Court the up to date position, having written the report a month earlier. He also would have made a recommendation about making a restriction order under S 41 Mental Health Act 1983.

24.1.5. On 22 July 1992 a case conference was held, attended by Dr Lomax as well as an assistant Psychologist, the Senior Occupational Therapist, a member of the nursing staff, and a social worker; they were all from Kneesworth House. In addition Dr Anderson, and a senior social worker and a member of the nursing staff, all from the Bracton Clinic, attended. It was agreed that a S 37 Mental Health Act 1983 recommendation was appropriate. A psychology report was prepared for the assessment meeting which showed significant cognitive deterioration. A ward assessment was also available for the meeting in which Christopher Clunis was noted to have improved while on the ward. Further action was agreed, notably to try and obtain details of his earlier hospital admissions and his police records. Such efforts met with no success.

24.2. INCIDENTS OF VIOLENCE

24.2.1. On 30 July 1992 Christopher Clunis became very irate when the social worker asked for permission to contact his family. On 15 August 1992 he punched a fellow patient who had provoked him.

24.2.2. On 14 August 1992 Dr Taylor made a prescribed form S 37 Mental Health Act 1983 recommendation in which he stated, "He suffers from paranoid schizophrenia.... When ill he has exhibited violent behaviour....Although his psychosis is coming under control with medication he shows little insight into the need for continuing treatment. He would not cooperate with treatment outside hospital and would be likely to relapse. He could again act in a dangerous way if he becomes floridly psychotic." Dr Lomax also made a S 37 recommendation on 17 August 1992 in which he stated, "Since his admission to hospital he has made some progress with treatment. However he remains without insight and would be unlikely to cooperate for any significant period with out-patient care. He would soon relapse and pose a further danger to others." These reports were prepared for the Court hearing on 17 August 1992.

COMMENT

It is of concern that these S 37 Mental Health Act 1983 formal reports were not prepared and available to the Court before the day of the Trial.

25.0. HEARING AT CROYDON CROWN COURT

25.1. 17 AUGUST 1992

21.5.1. On 3 June 1992 Christopher Clunis had been committed from Tower Bridge Magistrates' Court to the Inner London Crown Court. He instructed Solicitors who wrote to the Inner London Crown Court on 21 July 1992 stating that it appeared that Christopher Clunis should plead guilty to the charge although they did not have clear instructions from him. However they suggested that the case be listed in a month's time, without witnesses attending, so that a Psychiatric report and Probation report could be prepared. The case was transferred to Croydon Crown Court where it was listed "for plea" on 17 August 1992. This means that the case was due to be heard in Court when the indictment is put to the Defendant for him to plead. No witnesses are asked to attend because if the Defendant pleads guilty there is no need for witnesses to give evidence. If the Defendant pleads not guilty the case is adjourned for another date when witnesses are then asked to attend.

25.1.2. Counsel who prosecuted the case, Mr Roger Turner, gave evidence to us. He told us that, having read the papers, he realised that there was no medical evidence regarding the victim and he therefore decided to enquire about the absence of that evidence at Court. When he arrived at Court he spoke to the Case Clerk employed by the Crown Prosecution Service who apparently told him that there was no medical evidence in respect of the victim. It is clear from the Court Transcript that Roger Turner was aware that two memoranda had been sent from the Crown Prosecution Service to the Police asking them to obtain medical evidence in respect of the victim.

25.1.3. He also spoke at Court to a Police Officer, whom he thought was the Officer in charge of the case. In fact DC Owen told us that he did not attend Court on that day, but PC Anstead told us that he had attended. It appears therefore that Roger Turner's conversation at Court was with PC Anstead. The Officer told Roger Turner that the victim had disappeared. From the Court Transcript, it is clear that Roger Turner had been told by the Officer: that the victim had disappeared and the Police had not been able to obtain his consent to Guy's Hospital preparing a report on his injury and treatment; that despite the victim having stated in his signed statement that Guy's Hospital could release his medical records to the Police, in fact Guy's Hospital required a proper form of release signed by the patient before so doing. Roger Turner told us he was surprised at this but accepted what he was told by the Officer.

25.1.4. PC Anstead remembered attending Court on 17 August 1992. He understood the decision had already been made by the Crown Prosecution Service not to pursue the case before he went to Court. He could not recall any discussion with Counsel for the Prosecution.

25.1.5. Christopher Clunis was taken to Croydon Crown Court from Kneesworth House Hospital on the morning of 17 August 1992. He was seen there by his Counsel, Mr Anthony Rimmer. We have heard evidence from Mr Rimmer. He was a most impressive witness.

25.1.6. Anthony Rimmer told us that his Instructions were to attend Court on behalf of Christopher Clunis who wished to enter a plea of not guilty. However there seemed to be a suggestion in the papers that when Counsel had discussed the matter with his client, Christopher Clunis might take a different view. Anthony Rimmer arrived at Court and went to see Christopher Clunis in the cells. He was of the view that his client was not well, and was rather dull and obdurate, as though he were on medication. However he was perfectly satisfied that he could take instructions from him. He told us that although Christopher Clunis seemed sure he wished to plead not guilty, Anthony Rimmer felt that after full discussion and explanation, and after he had earned his client's confidence, Christopher Clunis "would probably have been receptive to entering a plea." He then had a discussion with Roger Turner about the lack of medical evidence in respect of the victim because he was concerned as to the extent of injury and as to whether the charge was properly brought under S 18 Offences Against the Person Act 1861. Roger Turner told him there was none and he also told him that the victim had disappeared.

25.1.7. The case was then called on in Court before His Honour Judge Pullinger. We have seen a transcript of what took place in Court. The Judge was told about the lack of medical evidence in respect of the victim and the fact that the victim had disappeared and agreed to the matter being adjourned shortly to enable Roger Turner and the Crown Prosecution Service to decide what course to take. Judge Pullinger asked for, and was provided with, copies of the medical reports in respect of Christopher Clunis. Those were the report prepared by Dr Lomax (from Kneesworth House Hospital) on 17 July 1992, and two S 37 Mental Health Act 1983 reports, one signed by Dr Taylor on 14 August 1992 and one signed by Dr Lomax on 17 August 1992. We have received evidence from Judge Pullinger who told us that since he only received the medical reports in respect of the Defendant during the hearing, he was not able to give the matter the consideration he would have liked. He thought that the reports should have been with the Court papers before the hearing so that he had time to consider them properly before the matter was called on.

25.1.8. Roger Turner told us that he had not seen any of those reports since they were confidential to the Defence. However from the Court transcript it is clear that it was he who produced to the Judge both a copy of Dr Taylor's report and a facsimiled copy of Dr Lomax's report dated 17 July 1992 . Anthony Rimmer told us that he and Roger Turner had gone through the medical reports together.

25.1.9. The Case Clerk telephoned the Principal Crown Prosecutor who advised that enquiry should be made as to whether the victim could be traced, so that an application for an adjournment could be made. However he also advised that if there was no likelihood of the victim being traced in the foreseeable future then the Prosecution should offer no evidence. It is clear from the Court transcript that Roger Turner spoke to the Officer who did not think it was likely that the victim would be traced within a reasonable time. Roger Turner told us that he spoke to the Principal Crown Prosecutor and in the light of the information that the victim had disappeared and was unlikely to be traced in the reasonably near future, it was considered that there was not a reasonable prospect of conviction. Roger Turner and the CPS decided that no evidence should be offered against Christopher Clunis. The matter was not discussed with those who were repsonsible for Christopher Clunis' care.

25.1.10. Anthony Rimmer put it this way: "My understanding was that the victim was effectively an itinerant, that it would have involved a lot of enquiry of hostels that he was known to frequent, and it really probably would have been a hopeless task at the end of the day, and of course, because Turner couldn't give a time estimation as to how long this would take, to have it listed for trial in a week's time, a month's time, it would probably have been an academic exercise and wouldn't have borne fruit."

25.1.11. In the light of that, Anthony Rimmer advised his client to plead not guilty when the Indictment was put to him. The case was called on again in Court and the Indictment was put to Christopher Clunis when he pleaded not guilty. Roger Turner then offered no evidence and a verdict of not guilty was recorded. Christopher Clunis was therefore free to walk from the dock.

25.1.12. Judge Pullinger told us that with hindsight he wished he had suggested to Counsel for the prosecution that the matter was adjourned to allow further enquiries. However he could not have directed an adjournment if the Crown did not consent.

25.1.13. Anthony Rimmer told us that he was very concerned about his client because the case had been dropped against him, and because he knew that there was no continuing Mental Health Order, so that his client would be released immediately. He knew the medical orderlies who had accompanied Christopher Clunis from Kneesworth House Hospital were on strict instructions to return with him there, but Anthony Rimmer was unsure that they had the power to do so, once he had been found not guilty. He asked Christopher Clunis what the regime was like at Kneesworth. His client said that he was comfortable and he was not troubled by it. In those circumstances, Anthony Rimmer did not ask for his client to be discharged from the dock. He told us that it was the only time in his professional career that he has not asked for a client, who has been acquitted, to be discharged, and he did not do so because he was so concerned about Christopher Clunis.

COMMENT

It seems to us that the Crown Prosecution Service were not made sufficiently aware of Christopher Clunis' mental illness and potential for violence. The Police thought he was mentally ill and had assessed him as very dangerous. As we understand matters, that information was not passed to the Crown Prosecution Service. HMP Belmarsh knew he was seriously mentally ill. We do not think the information that they possessed was passed to the Crown Prosecution Service. The medical reports were only available to the Court on the day of the Trial. They were not sent to the Crown Prosecution Service. We were told that it is not the role of the Crown Prosecution Service to consider the question of a Defendant's dangerousness in deciding whether there is sufficient evidence to prove the case against the Defendant.

We consider that there was a vital lack of communication at this critical stage in Christopher Clunis' care. It was only because of Anthony Rimmer's concerns and Christopher Clunis' desire to return to Kneesworth House to collect his belongings, that he did not walk away from the Court and from every type of help or care at that time.

We agree with Judge Pullinger that, with hindsight, it would have been better to adjourn the case so that further inquiries could have been made as to the whereabouts of the victim.

26.0. FROM KNEESWORTH HOUSE HOSPITAL TO GUY'S HOSPITAL

26.1. 17 AUGUST 1992

26.1.1. Dr Lomax was Christopher Clunis' Responsible Medical Officer until mid August 1992 when he transferred to another ward at Kneesworth House. Dr Bernard Heine, Locum Consultant Psychiatrist, then became Christopher Clunis' Responsible Medical Officer. It appears from the medical records that Dr Heine became Christopher Clunis' Responsible Medical Officer on 14 August 1992 since a detailed note of his history is made on that date.

26.1.2. After the case was dismissed against him Christopher Clunis agreed to return as an informal patient to Kneesworth House. On arrival it was decided that he should be detained in hospital under S 3 Mental Health Act 1983 and two doctors and a social worker were asked to provide recommendations for that purpose. A detention order under S.3 Mental Health Act 1983 was made, the diagnosis being paranoid schizophrenia. Dr Chalmers Fleming of St Andrew's Hospital, Northampton signed one medical recommendation on 17 August 1992, in which he stated that Christopher Clunis expressed no regret for the offence "claiming his action was perfectly normal and that he would repeat this if he found himself in similar circumstances." He considered that Christopher Clunis would be likely to discharge himself if an informal patient. He continued, "Until his treatment is stabilised he represents a serious potential threat to others whom he feels are slighting or otherwise interfering with his affairs." Dr Kanakaratnam of Fairfield Hospital, Hitchin, Hertfordshire made the second recommendation on 18 August 1992. He described Christopher Clunis as "impulsively and dangerously aggressive having recently knifed a room mate in the neck...He lacks insight into his illness and feels his offence was justifiable." He considered that in view of Christopher Clunis' known dangerousness "he needs further treatment in a secure setting on a formal basis."

26.1.2. On 20 August 1992 the Wood Green Office of Haringey Social Services was telephoned by Kneesworth House Hospital and asked to send a social worker to visit Christopher Clunis at that Hospital for the purposes of recommending a Detention Order under S.3 Mental Health Act 1983. Wood Green were asked to make the assessment because Christopher Clunis' had given his last known address as 1 Burleigh Road London N.8, which fell within Haringey catchment area. Mr Julian Green was asked to visit. We have heard evidence from Julian Green. He is a graduate, with a social work qualification and he is also an Approved Social Worker for the purposes of S. 12 Mental Health Act 1983.

26.1.3. Julian Green visited Christopher Clunis at Kneesworth House on the same day. He told Julian Green about the stabbing incident at Lancelot Andrewes House saying that it was out of character, "I've never been involved with anything like this...I wish I'd never done it and I feel I've learnt a lot from that." Julian Green spoke to the staff at the Hospital who said that Christopher Clunis kept changing his mind as to whether he would stay in hospital on an informal basis. Julian Green recommended that he be the subject of a S.3 Order and told Christopher Clunis that Haringey Social Services would help him when he came back to live in their area. He told us that he read the two medical recommendations that had already been made and he was happy to make his own recommendation. In particular he was struck by Christopher Clunis' lack of insight into the offence and apparent lack of remorse and he thought "he was potentially still dangerous." Julian Green was not given copies of the medical recommendations nor of his own recommendation; he told us it was customary not to do so.

26.2. CONTACT WITH THE BRACTON CLINIC

26.2.1. Dr Anderson told us that Dr Lomax contacted him at the Bracton Clinic to inform him of what had occurred at Court and that Christopher Clunis had since been detained under S 3 Mental Health Act 1983. Dr Anderson asked Dr Lomax what level of security Christopher Clunis needed and he recalled Dr Lomax saying that Christopher Clunis could now be managed within the general psychiatric service. Dr Lomax had no recollection of any contact with the Bracton Clinic after the Court hearing until he was reminded of it by learning of the evidence of Dr Anderson. He then told us that it remained his view, after the Court hearing, that Christopher Clunis was still a potential danger and he does not recall suggesting that he should be admitted to a General Psychiatric Ward. He pointed out that the S 37 Mental Health Act 1983 recommendation given by him on 17 August 1992 referred to Christopher Clunis being at risk of a relapse and then a danger to others. He could not accept that Dr Anderson's recollection was correct on that point.

26.2.2. A decision was however made to transfer him to the General Psychiatric Ward at Guy's Hospital. Dr Lomax said that the transfer to Guy's occurred in the following circumstances. He told us that he had received a telephone call from Guy's Hospital to say that they wanted to admit Christopher Clunis to Guy's on the following day, since he was no longer a forensic case and he was detained by virtue of S 3 Mental Health Act 1983 (a civil section). That was the first time that Dr Lomax knew Guy's Hospital had anything to do with Christopher Clunis; he thought the Bracton Clinic was the referring hospital. Dr Lomax was surprised at the request and the speed of the transfer. On 20 August 1992 Dr Lomax informed the Ashwell Unit that Christopher Clunis was to be transferred to Robert Gillespie Ward, York Clinic, Guy's Hospital on the following day. Dr Lomax told us that at Kneesworth they had decided to try to establish Christopher Clunis on depot injections but were unable to start that treatment before his transfer to Guy's Hospital. We were also told by Dr Lomax that Christopher Clunis had not been given occupational therapy while at Kneesworth House because he had not, by the time of his discharge, reached the stage where he would have been receptive to such therapy. Had he remained at Kneesworth House he would have been given a long rehabilitation programme to ensure that he could cope within the community on discharge.

26.2.3. On 21 August 1992 Christopher Clunis was transferred to the York Clinic at Guy's Hospital and Dr Heine sent a discharge summary, and copies of the Admission Summary and Court report prepared by Dr Lomax.

26.2.4. We have heard evidence from Dr McCarthy, Consultant Psychiatrist at Guy's Hospital. According to him, the transfer was arranged during a telephone call between him and Dr Lomax on 17 August 1992. Dr McCarthy assumed that Dr Lomax was a forensic psychiatrist as he had been treating the patient in a secure unit. In the course of the telephone call Dr McCarthy said he was informed by Dr Lomax of the events at Croydon Crown Court and that Christopher Clunis' mental state was vastly improved and was almost normal. Dr Lomax suggested (according to Dr McCarthy) that Christopher Clunis be detained under S.3 Mental Health Act 1983. Dr McCarthy told us he felt very ambivalent about that suggestion, but agreed so that Christopher Clunis would not just walk out of hospital. Dr McCarthy's misgivings related to the fact that he was being told by Dr Lomax on the one hand that Christopher Clunis was almost normal and yet on the other hand, Dr Lomax was suggesting a detention Order. Dr McCarthy understood Dr Lomax to be saying that Christopher Clunis needed to be in hospital but no longer in a secure unit. Dr Lomax does not recall talking to Dr McCarthy in those terms. Neither made a note of the telephone call.

26.3. COMMENT

Julian Green considered that it would be sensible for Social Services to have copies of all the recommendations to be kept in the client's file. We agree. Similarly, with hindsight Julian Green considered that it would be sensible for him to have written a report and sent it to Kneesworth House and to the two Doctors who had made the medical recommendations so that all were informed of the position. We agree.

We find it very difficult to come to any clear conclusions as to how and why Christopher Clunis was transferred and with such speed from Kneesworth House to Guy's Hospital. We are very concerned that the decision was made after little consideration and probably in the interests of saving money. Such a decision was made at the expense of the patient, Christopher Clunis, since he was not given time to adjust, no plan was formulated and there was little contact with those who had been caring for him for the previous 3 months. Above all, the views of the doctors who made the S 3 Mental Health Act 1983 recommendations were paid scant regard, if not wholly ignored. For whatever reason the transfer occurred, we consider that the decision to transfer Christopher Clunis to the General Psychiatric Services at that time was wrong. We consider that he should have remained in a secure unit until there was no longer a risk of dangerous behaviour.

We find it difficult to accept that Dr Lomax in fact suggested the transfer to Guy's. On balance we feel that Dr McCarthy must have been the prime mover in the decision. He may well have relied on the facts that no S 37 Mental Health Act 1983 Order was imposed at the Court; that Christopher Clunis was not convicted of any charge; and that he understood that Christopher Clunis had improved and was now detained only under a "civil section" of the Mental Health Act 1983, namely S 3. We repeat, we consider the decision was ill considered and wrong. In our view the fact that the Crown Court case had failed should not have obscured the fact that, for medical reasons, Christopher Clunis needed care and treatment in secure accommodation.

We comment again on the need to make a contemporaneous record of events relating to a patient, so that, at the very least, those who care for the patient afterwards know what steps have been taken.

27.0. GUY'S HOSPITAL

27.1. 21 AUGUST 1992 TO 24 SEPTEMBER 1992

27.1.1. Christopher Clunis was transferred to the York Clinic, Guy's Hospital, 117 Borough High Street, London SE1 on 21 August 1992 under the care of Dr Anthony

McCarthy, Consultant General Psychiatrist. Dr McCarthy had agreed previously with HMP Belmarsh that he would be the named catchment area Consultant to provide aftercare when Christopher Clunis was discharged from the secure Unit. We have heard evidence from Dr McCarthy and from his Research Fellow, Dr Kamal Gupta.

27.1.2. When Christopher Clunis was transferred from Kneesworth House Hospital a copy of the Court report prepared by Dr Lomax dated 17 July 1992, and a letter to Dr Gupta dated 21 August 1992 from Dr Heine, were sent to Guy's plus copies of the S 3 Mental Health Act 1983 medical recommendations and a Nursing Discharge summary. Dr Heine referred in those documents to the attempts made while Christopher Clunis was at Kneesworth to obtain information from hospitals where he had been treated previously, but stated that such attempts had thus far proved fruitless. Guy's were already in possession of a letter dated 19 May 1992 written by Dr O'Neill-Byrne (Research Fellow in Psychiatry at HM Prison Belmarsh) setting out his history; a nursing assessment from HMP Belmarsh dated 18 May 1992; and also an assessment report dated 6 May 1992 from Dr Tim Exworthy, Court Liaison Psychiatrist at Tower Bridge Magistrates' Court.

27.1.3. Dr McCarthy said he was surprised by the terms of the S.3 Mental Health Act 1983 recommendations as they were not consistent with what he had been told by Dr Lomax or the fact that Christopher Clunis was not to be cared for within a regional secure unit. He placed greater reliance on what Dr Lomax told him in the telephone call, as Dr Lomax had been the Consultant responsible for the care of Christopher Clunis. He did not contact Dr Lomax to discuss the matter further. Dr McCarthy told us that he treats many patients on his general psychiatric ward who have committed violent offences for which they show no remorse, and that in his view such features "do not necessarily link with a psychotic illness."

27.2. INPATIENT AT GUY'S HOSPITAL

27.2.1. On admission to Guy's, Christopher Clunis' insight was noted to be poor and he did not want to talk about the stabbing offence. On 25 August 1992 when Dr Gupta began to discuss the need for an injection, Christopher Clunis threatened him and left the interview. He was seen by Edgar Jones, a Psychotherapist, on 26 August 1992 when it was noted that he preferred not to talk about the incident which led to his admission. Christopher Clunis said he was now well and willing to take medication. He was described as articulate and intelligent and that he was keen to study for a degree. He said he would not abuse drugs again and that his principal concern was to find accommodation. Diabetes was diagnosed on 26 August 1992.

27.2.2. By the 7 September his mental state was said to be appropriate although he tended to be overfamiliar, especially with female staff. On 10 September 1992 his mental state was described as normal and his disinhibition before females was put down to his personality. The nursing staff recorded that he was angry and abusive on that day. He was given leave of absence on 13 September 1992 and on subsequent days to try and sort out his accommodation and financial benefits for the time when he was discharged. On 14 September 1992 Dr Gupta wrote to the Homeless Persons Unit on Christopher Clunis' behalf, asking for their help in accommodating him. Dr Gupta described him as a person with a long psychiatric history who had been psychologically stable since his admission to Guy's and who "behaves in a reasonable and responsible manner". He said he was fit for discharge as soon as housing became available. Dr McCarthy told us that in his view Christopher Clunis was violent when psychotic but that he could be aggressive and assertive at other times, which he felt was part of Christopher Cliunis' underlying personality. Christopher Clunis was given bed and breakfast accommodation in Haringey on 14 September 1992 for 1 week until 20 September 1992. Nevertheless he remained on the Ward at Guy's Hospital. On 21 September 1992 he was noted to be aggressive and pressing for his discharge because he did not want to lose his accommodation. He was given leave until 24 September 1992 when he was to return for the S 117 meeting. He returned for the meeting and was discharged on 24 September 1992 from S 3 Mental Health Act 1983 and Guy's Hospital.

27.3. DISCHARGE FROM GUY'S HOSPITAL – 24 SEPTEMBER 1992

27.3.1. Dr McCarthy told us that in his view, and that of his team, Christopher Clunis was dangerous and could be unpleasant when taunted, but was very pleasant and affable most of the time. Dr Gupta and Dr McCarthy knew Christopher Clunis was aggressive from time to time. Dr Gupta said "I must state that underlying all of this there was always a feeling that there is something amiss about this person... He presents in that kind of an aggressive way and he just all the time made me feel that he would be best followed up by forensic services because of his underlying personality and if he does relapse. He was certainly going to be a difficult one to be taken up by the ordinary psychiatric service, by the community psychiatric services etc." Dr McCarthy thought he understood why Christopher Clunis was aggressive; he was being detained when the case against him had been dropped and he was now well; but Dr McCarthy told us that, in his view, Christopher Clunis' aggression had other components. Similarly Dr Gupta spoke of the pressure he was put under by Christopher Clunis to be discharged in the circumstances that he was, as Dr Gupta described him, "completely well".

27.3.2. Hence Dr McCarthy and Dr Gupta felt that Christopher Clunis needed some forensic follow up when he was discharged. It was agreed that Dr Gupta would try to organise that. We were told by Dr Parrott and Dr Anderson at the Bracton Clinic that they had been telephoned by Dr Gupta and they suggested that a forensic follow up would be sensible. They were not asked to arrange that.

27.3.3. Dr Gupta telephoned the forensic department at Friern Hospital and spoke to Dr de Taranto (Senior House Officer to the Consultant Forensic Psychiatrist, Dr Kennedy) telling her the history and asking for Christopher Clunis to be followed up by the forensic services. Dr Gupta's contemporaneous note reads: "She will discuss with Dr Kennedy and will call back *mane* re O.P. [outpatient] appointment". She rang back to say that, since he was presently being cared for on an open ward by the general psychiatrists, that he should be referred to the general psychiatrist who would refer him to the forensic team if necessary. Dr Gupta did not make a note of the second telephone call. Dr Gupta said it was the only occasion that he had made a forensic referral in such informal terms. He agreed that a more formal approach is usual and with hindsight considered that the informal approach was not taken seriously.

27.3.4. We heard evidence from Dr Henry Kennedy, now Consultant in Forensic Psychiatry at Camlet Lodge Secure Unit, Chase Farm Hospital, The Ridgeway,

Enfield, Middlesex. At the time with which we are concerned, he was Consultant Forensic Psychiatrist at Friern Hospital.

27.3.5. He told us that on 21st September 1992 Dr de Taranto, Dr Kennedy's Senior House Officer, was telephoned by Dr Gupta of Guy's Hospital. She spoke to Dr Kennedy about the 'phone call and he advised her to write down what she remembered of the call. He did this because he was concerned at the unusual nature of the call. The note made by Dr de Taranto has been shown to us. It indicates that Dr Gupta gave her a short history of Christopher Clunis and informed her of his new address, and said that he was now due for discharge under S.117 Mental Health Act 1983. Dr Gupta said that he had made an appointment with Dr Seargeant for 9 October 1992 and was asking whether Christopher Clunis could be given a forensic appointment also.

27.3.6. Dr Kennedy told us the request was highly unusual. He told us that normally when a patient is referred to him from outside his area by another team he would be given the full history, the record of previous convictions, and he would be asked to assess the patient. In addition a comprehensive aftercare plan would be formulated between them and discussion would take place as to when the discharge would be appropriate. He had never come across a request like this from a general psychiatric service, on the telephone, without a full history, without information as to his criminal record, when the patient was not in his catchment area, when no assessment was requested and when an appointment with Dr Seargeant had already been fixed. He said he had frequent dealings with Guy's forensic services and he was sure that had the referral come from them it would have been in the way he described and not at all in the way adopted by Dr Gupta.

27.3.7. Dr Kennedy informed us that he told Dr de Taranto to tell Dr Gupta that the patient should attend the appointment with the general psychiatric services who would refer the patient to the forensic services if necessary. Dr de Taranto then telephoned Dr Gupta and, as she noted in her contemporaneous record, told Dr Gupta that the patient should attend Dr Seargeant's outpatient appointment and he would then be referred to the forensic team if necessary. Dr Gupta according to Dr de Taranto's note agreed to send a copy of the discharge summary to the forensic team. In the event none was sent by Guy's.

27.3.8. Dr Gupta told us that he then telephoned the General Psychiatric Service at Friern Hospital and spoke to Dr Seargeant, Associate Specialist. He could not recall the conversation precisely and he made no contemporaneous record of the call. Dr Gupta insists that he had the conversation with Dr Seargeant after his telephone calls to Dr de Taranto and Dr McCarthy confirms that view. However having seen the note made by Dr de Taranto we feelbound to conclude that Dr Gupta had spoken to Dr Seargeant previously and had already fixed the outpatient appointment with Dr Seargeant by the time he telephoned the forensic services. Dr Gupta accepted that he had not told Dr Seargeant during that telephone call that she was to be the named S.117 Mental Health Act 1983 keyworker. He said that the discharge was made difficult because Christopher Clunis was moving out of the area. He also said that Christopher Clunis had always indicated that he did not want social work help after his discharge. He said it is difficult to provide for a patient who does not want help.

27.3.9. Dr Janet Seargeant is an Associate Specialist in Psychiatry at Friern Hospital and we have heard evidence from her. She told us that on 21 September 1992 Dr Gupta (from Guy's Hospital) telephoned the out-patient department of Friern Hospital asking for an out patient appointment for Christopher Clunis who was being cared for in Guy's Hospital but who wanted to live in Haringey. The nurse who took the call passed the telephone to Dr Seargeant because she was unsure whether the patient came within the catchment area for Friern Hospital. Dr Seargeant made notes of the telephone call which we have seen.

27.3.10. According to Dr Seargeant, she was asked to make an appointment for Christopher Clunis who was going to live in the Haringey area. She was told he suffered from paranoid schizophrenia, that he had been to prison for assaulting another resident at a hostel, that he was then cared for at Kneesworth House Hospital from where he had gone to Guy's Hospital under a S.3 Mental Health Act 1983 Detention Order. She was told by Dr Gupta that the patient was now "completely well", that he was to be discharged from the Detention Order, that a S.117 Mental Health Act after-care meeting was to take place on 24 September 1992 before he was to be discharged from Guy's Hospital, and his medication was described. Dr Seargeant told us that the dose was very low. Dr Gupta asked for an out patient appointment for Christopher Clunis and said he would send a letter about the patient to the out patient department at Friern Hospital. An appointment was made for 9 October 1992 for Christopher Clunis to be seen by Dr Taylor. Dr Seargeant could not recall whether Dr Gupta told her he had asked for a forensic appointment, but she made no note thereof and in our view it is unlikely that it was mentioned to her. With hindsight Dr Seargeant now feels that she should not have agreed to give an outpatient appointment without insisting that a member of Haringey Social Services should attend the proposed S 117 Meeting.

27.3.11. Dr Gupta told us that he and the team were influenced by the fact that Christopher Clunis was given leave of absence from Guy's and always returned therefrom, that he found himself accommodation, that he registered with a General Practitioner, and was taking his medication. He agreed that there was always the possibility of a relapse and that had Christopher Clunis remained in the Southwark area a Community Psychiatric Nurse would have been involved in his aftercare.

27.4. S.117 MENTAL HEALTH ACT MEETING AT GUY'S HOSPITAL

27.4.1. Dr Gupta told us that he was present at the S 117 Mental Health Act 1983 meeting held on 24 September 1992 when Christopher Clunis, the Social Worker (Ann Witham) and probably a nurse also attended. Dr McCarthy did not attend and Dr Seargeant from Friern Hospital was not invited to attend, nor was anyone from Haringey Social Services. Dr Gupta said that no plan was written down although a plan was formulated at the meeting and Christopher Clunis knew what the plan was. We were never told what the plan comprised. He said that an outpatient appointment had been arranged at Friern Hospital for 9 October 1992 at 10.30 am. He could not precisely recall how Dr Seargeant came to be named as the keyworker or whether it was discussed with her. He thought he would have told her but he could not say when. He agreed that no name was put down for the General Practitioner. He did not think a copy of the S 117 forms had been sent to the G.P. He agreed that the form was lacking in the information it should have contained.

27.4.2. It was apparently decided that no social work involvement was necessary for Christopher Clunis' aftercare. He agreed that with hindsight they had gone along with what Christopher Clunis wanted to a greater extent than they should have done, that they should have insisted on social work involvement, and either followed him up themselves or made more comprehensive arrangements for his follow up.

27.4.3. Dr Gupta accepted that the S 117 Mental Health Act 1983 aftercare plan did not follow the protocol then laid down by Guys and St Thomas's Hospitals but he and Dr McCarthy said there were major difficulties in following the protocol. Dr McCarthy described the serious shortfall in resources available to them to provide proper aftercare although he said social work provision had improved dramatically since 1992. He said that it was difficult if not impossible to carry out a S 117 Mental Health Act 1983 aftercare plan in accordance with the protocol because patients only stay on his ward for an average of 18 days.

27.5. DISCHARGE SUMMARY

27.5.1. The discharge summary was not sent to Friern Hospital until about 6 November 1992. Dr McCarthy acknowledged that the system had fallen down in that respect but told us that the Senior House Officer was away ill, and Dr Gupta had dictated a summary and left it with his then temporary secretary, who typed it and kept it until Dr Gupta returned from his annual leave. Hence it was not sent to Friern until Dr Gupta returned to Guy's at the end of October, when it was then signed by him and Dr McCarthy. It had clearly not been sent by the time of the outpatient appointment arranged for Christopher Clunis at Friern on 9 October 1992. Dr McCarthy told us that he has now introduced a new system so that the date when the discharge summary is sent is recorded, and the full summary is expected to be sent within 2 weeks of discharge. Also a form has been devised which is completed at the time of discharge and one copy is given to the General Practitioner, one to the patient, one is kept in the notes and one is given to the Pharmacy. He gave us a copy of the new form which sets out vital information in relation to a patient including the diagnosis, the aftercare plan, likely problems, and medication.

27.5.2. The discharge summary in respect of Christopher Clunis, which is undated, stated that attempts to obtain his records from earlier hospital admissions were unsuccessful. Dr Gupta was unable to tell us what steps had been taken to obtain the records and no note of any request or the result of such request is included in the records. Dr Gupta thought it was possible that no further attempts had been made to obtain the earlier records and that they had relied on the Kneesworth attempts, although he thought that was unlikely. Both he and Dr McCarthy said that there were well known problems in obtaining earlier records.

27.6. SOCIAL WORK INVOLVEMENT

27.6.1. While Christopher Clunis was in Guy's Hospital, he was first referred to the Hospital's Department of Social Work on 28 August 1992 for a small cash grant. After this initial brief contact, his case was closed. His home address on the referral form was added at a later date and was said to be 5 Malbro Road, Wood Green,

N22. This must have been added after he was referred on 2 September 1992 to the social worker on the psychiatric ward, Ann Witham, for help to find accommodation on his discharge from Hospital. She gave evidence to us. She told us that she always worked as part of the Psychiatric Team and that all decisions were made collectively.

27.6.2. Ann Witham said that she helped Christopher Clunis obtain housing in Haringey and to secure appropriate benefits. She wrote to the Homeless Persons Unit on 9 September 1992 describing his discharge from psychiatric hospital and stating that previously he had been of no fixed abode. In the letter she said that he had been sleeping rough since September 1991 and was anxious to return to Haringey where he would have the support of his extended family; and that none of his family could have him to live with them. It appears that all this information came from Christopher Clunis and that none of it was checked, because Christopher Clunis was reluctant to provide more detailed information. She did not discuss his history or the accuracy thereof with a doctor but she participated in ward round discussions. She did not make contact with the Approved Social Worker in Haringey, Julian Green, who had made the recommendation for Christopher Clunis' detention under S 3 Mental Health Act 1983, as a result of which he had been admitted to Guy's Hospital. She regarded her involvement with him as primarily to help with practical needs, and she was impressed by his demonstrated ability to make his own arrangements in Haringey. She said Christopher Clunis was very independent and she respected that. She acknowledged that she did not record her discussions with him regarding his preferences for aftercare arrangements.

27.6.3. On 14th September 1992 he was given leave of absence to try and sort out some accommodation. He was given bed and breakfast accommodation and on 15 September 1992 told the social work assistant that the address was 5 Malbro Road, Wood Green, London N 22. Ann Witham could not explain how the address came to be recorded as 112 Marlboro Road on the S. 117 form or why the correct address of 112 Marlborough Road was never recorded anywhere. She had been at the S.117 meeting. She had spoken to Christopher Clunis before the meeting and he was adamant that he did not want any social work involvement nor any aftercare in the form of day centre or the like. She was strongly influenced by the fact that he had sorted out his accommodation, had registered with a General Practitioner, had always returned to the ward after leave of absence, and was taking his medication. She agreed with him that no social work involvement was necessary after he was discharged, and relied on his assertion that he would seek out such help if he wanted it. She was surprised when she was told by the Inquiry Panel that Christopher Clunis had not known how to open a bank account so that he could obtain the benefit of a cheque for nearly £350 which had been passed to him by the social work assistant on 16 September 1992. Ann Witham wrote to the Social Services Department at Haringey on 23 September 1992 stating that he was to be discharged and that, "He is quite capable of self care and should be able to cope with independent living....I do not feel that there is a need for any social work intervention with Mr Clunis at present..." Ann Witham said that although she wrote the letter, the decision that he did not need Social Work intervention was made by the multi-disciplinary team caring for Christopher Clunis although she made no note of the fact that the decision was a collective one.

27.6.4. Ann Witham told us that had she known about Christopher Clunis' violent history she would have referred him to Haringey Social Services and would not have respected his strong wish not to have any social work involvement.

27.7. GUY'S INTERNAL INQUIRY

27.7.1. An internal inquiry was carried out at Guy's Hospital on 10 February 1993. The inquiry meeting highlighted the shortage of medium secure unit facilities. It also concluded that the care of Christopher Clunis on the Ward was of a high standard and the aftercare arrangements were exemplary. Dr McCarthy told us he did not agree with that view; it was "ridiculous". He had however been present at the meeting. He considered that the Serious Incidents Committee sometimes made their investigative role subordinate to their supportive role. The committee and the way it is run is currently being changed now that the Mental health Unit is becoming a Trust in its own right.

27.8. GUY'S MENTAL HEALTH MANAGER

27.8.1. We have heard evidence from Mr Kent, Guy's Mental Health Manager. He told us that the original S.117 protocol, which we have seen, that was in use in 1992 has now been scrapped as it was realised it had some serious shortcomings. We agree that the original S.117 protocol seemed to be more concerned with procedure than with providing proper aftercare for patients. Mr Kent considered that the new Protocol which was also produced for us was now much better.

COMMENT

We consider that the decision to discharge Christopher Clunis at that time was ill considered and ill prepared. Dr Parrott or Dr Anderson should have been asked to see Christopher Clunis to advise on his future management. Contact with Friern Hospital was almost non-existent and certainly insufficient to ensure that his care was properly transferred.

In our view the S 117 Mental Health Act 1983 aftercare plan was also virtually non existent. No details had been formulated, neither was the plan divulged to Friern Hospital, nor to Haringey Social Services, nor to the General Practitioner, all of whom were then supposed to take responsibility for his care. The discharge summary was sent to Friern Hospital and then took about 6 weeks to arrive. We do not consider that was good enough and, because of the delay, Friern Hospital was not alerted to the need for prompt action. We consider this a serious failure by Dr McCarthy and his team. We are very concerned at the care given to Christopher Clunis by the General Psychiatric Team and the Social Worker in discharging him to another Borough when so little contact, communication or liaison had been effected. We are sure that Christopher Clunis was entitled to better care than he received and that the risk of his danger to the public was not properly assessed.

In our view, Ann Witham as a member of the ward multi-disciplinary team should have found out more about Christopher Clunis before making any recommendation about his future care. She was told us very clearly how much she was guided by his own preferences as well as his own account of his past. She helped him to make contact with the Housing department, a General practitioner, and to obtain benefits. However she and the Pscyhiatric Team then relied on him for details of names and addresses, several of which were inaccurately recorded or left blank on his S 117 Mental Health Act 1983 aftercare plan. In setting down in writing to Haringey Social Services on 23 September 1992 that there was no need for social work intervention at present, we consider that the Psychiatric Team, through Ann Witham, gave groundless reassurance which contributed crucially to subsequent doubt, delay and under reaction.

As regards the Internal Inquiry we feel that it hardly needs pointing out that any such Inquiry must be as objective as possible if it is to serve any useful purpose for the future. It seems to us that the Internal Inquiry did subordinate its investigative, critical role to its supportive role. We deplore that.

28.0. HARINGEY – HOUSING EMERGENCY GROUP FOR THE

28.1. HOMELESS – SEPTEMBER 1992

28.1.1. The Emergency Housing Group of Haringey Social Services at Apex House, 820 Seven Sisters Road, London N 15 caters for Homeless people in the Borough. We have heard evidence from Mr Kieran Gillan, Case worker within the Group and from Mr Peter West, now Assistant Director for Adult Services of Haringey Housing and Social Services, who was at the relevant time Housing Co-ordinator for the Homeless Service. The Housing Group identifies and assesses homeless people and then arranges accommodation for people who fulfil the relevant criteria. Temporary accommodation is provided until various matters have been checked to ensure the person's identity and that they are homeless and that Haringey is responsible for them.

28.1.2. Peter West told us that homelessness is a real problem in Haringey, that they have 3,000 homeless households in temporary accommodation and that they have 50 new applications each week.

28.1.3. On 14 September 1992 Christopher Clunis attended the Housing Emergency Group asking for accommodation. He brought with him a letter written by Dr Gupta, which we have referred to above, in which Dr Gupta from Guy's Hospital described him as a person with a long psychiatric history who "behaves in a reasonable and responsible manner". In addition he brought a letter from Anne Witham, of Southwark Social Services, to which we have also referred above, in which she described him as "vulnerable". She stated, "Mr Clunis' last address in Haringey was 26 Turnpike Lane, N5, where he lived for 3 years up until September 1991. This was private rented accommodation and Mr Clunis had to leave when the owner developed the property into a public house." That was a complete fiction, which we assume Anne Witham obtained from Christopher Clunis. She also said that "he will have the support of his extended family who still live in the area." Again that was not something she had checked, although it was in fact correct that Christopher Clunis' sister would offer some support to her brother.

28.1.4. Christopher Clunis was interviewed by the Housing Group; he gave them the name and address of his sister and the name and address of Lancelot Andrewes House. He was given bed and breakfast accommodation within the Maidstone Property Group and was told to go to the Head Office to be allocated a property and to collect the keys. He was given accommodation at 112D Marlborough Road, London N22. On 16 September 1992 he filled in a form in respect of special housing needs in which he gave his address as 5 Marlborough Road, although this was at some time changed to 112 Marlborough Road. On 17 September 1992 his name was logged on the Housing Emergency Group computer and he was assigned a number. A further appointment was made for him to see Kieran Gillan on 26 October 1992, when he was asked to bring in such supporting evidence as he had. Kieran Gillan told us that a 6 week time gap between the client attending the Housing Group and being assessed was normal in 1992 but it was realised that it was too long. The system has therefore now been changed and new clients are assessed within a matter of days of their first attending the Housing Emergency Group. On 28 September 1992 Christopher Clunis was assessed by the medical needs section as a vulnerable person.

28.1.5. Peter West told us that had the Housing Group been informed of Christopher Clunis' violent history, they would have told John Vanner before placing him in accommodation with the Maidstone Property Group. He said the issue of confidentiality was a real problem, particularly in relation to HIV and AIDS and, to a certain extent, decisions were made piecemeal. He felt very strongly that Guy's had given them wholly inadequate information. We agree.

29.0. 112 MARLBOROUGH ROAD

29.1. SEPTEMBER 1992

29.1.1. Christopher Clunis went to live at 112 Marlborough Road on 24 September 1992. We have heard evidence from Mr John Vanner who owns that property and also another 40 to 50 properties. From what we have heard it appears that John Vanner runs a good organisation under his personal control. Kieran Gillan told us that John Vanner is considered a trustworthy proprietor who is concerned with the welfare of people who stay in his property. John Vanner told us that 112D was a self contained studio flat with its own bedroom, lounge, shower, lavatory and cooking facilities and fridge. Gas and electricity were provided as were food including milk, bacon and eggs for breakfast. A cleaning service, 24 hour emergency service and visits from a Manager of the Group were also provided. John Vanner showed us a photograph of the house and it appeared a well constructed and maintained property.

29.1.2. John Vanner told us that he is given no information about the person whom he has to accommodate. He does not know if they have a history of mental illness, nor is he told of any history of violence. He makes his own assessment. He felt that the number of people that he housed who were mentally ill had increased over the years. He said that was his layman's opinion and he described such people, including Christopher Clunis as "slow". He said that he was willing to help provide more care although it was only very rarely that he was asked to do so. He was happy to provide meals, encourage washing and bathing, and keep an eye on someone if the Housing department asked him to do so. He felt that was a help in providing care in the community. He was not asked to provide such a service for Christopher Clunis.

29.1.3. Christopher Clunis picked up the keys from the Maidstone Property Group booking office. John Vanner explained that although the address is 112D Marlborough Road, above the door there is a sign which reads 5 Sydney Mansions, which was probably put there when the house was built many years ago. However the Maidstone Property Group does not own 5 Marlborough Road and never has. He told us that the Group has dual keys for each flat so that they can put the breakfast food in the tenant's fridge once a week. He told us that his Group cleans the communal parts of the House once every week and offers to clean the tenant's flat and change the sheets. A Manager attends the property at least 3 times a week to check the property is properly maintained, for example that the lights are working and there is no rubbish. The Manager knocks on each tenant's door and goes inside to make sure all is in order. He told us that he relied on his maintenance team to be his eyes and ears, to pick up if something is going wrong.

29.1.4. John Vanner remembered Christopher Clunis and had seen him at the property when he went to check it. He visited every fortnight. He often found the flat in a mess and occasionally they tidied it up. He told us, "But Christopher was the sort of person who, in a very short period of time, could turn round a good few hours work. It was amazing how quick it could deteriorate back to how it was." They did not feel the need to report him for untidiness, and in any event John Vanner told us they try to encourage tenants to keep the place tidy rather than report them. The only time he reports tenants is if they have created a health hazard. He said Christopher Clunis' room did look a mess but as there was no health hazard and they tried to encourage Christopher Clunis to tidy up, it was not something that worried him unduly. Neither he nor his staff saw anything that gave them cause for concern in respect of Christopher Clunis.

29.1.5. John Vanner told us that Christopher Clunis seemed rather a lonely man to him. He said that when he attended the property Christopher Clunis would put his head round the door, say "hello" and have a little chat. John Vanner did not find him intimidating. He said that Christopher Clunis stayed in the flat for long periods of time but he felt that had someone suggested a visit to a day centre or some other activity, Christopher Clunis would have gone. "I don't think you'd have met any resistance from him, but he didn't have the get up and go, to go and sort that...out for himself...He might have felt pressured by such a small thing like the Council Civic Centre, with all its noticeboards." He did not notice that Christopher Clunis changed over the period he was with them.

29.2. FAMILY INVOLVEMENT

29.2.1. Christopher Clunis' sister told us that she went to visit her brother at 112 Marlborough Road. She told us it was a nice property, near to shops and in a quiet road. She used to go with her daughter to take him groceries and cigarettes and clean up his rooms. She told us he used to get it in a dreadful state.

29.2.2. He showed her a cheque he had been given by Social Security for over £300 when he left Guy's Hospital but he did not know how to cash it. She tried to pay it into a bank for him but with no success because by 1992 it was no longer possible to pay in a third party cheque. She told him to take it back to the Hospital for them to sort out. She told us he could not open an account himself because first of all no one would have looked at him the way he was dressed and secondly he had no identification.

29.2.3. She said she visited Marlborough Road 4 or 5 times and that she saw him a week before the murder. She felt he was quiet on that occasion but nothing out of the ordinary.

29.2.4. Superintendent Barker made enquiries about 112 Marlborough Road, and discovered that the only person placed there by Haringey Housing Service was Christopher Clunis. She described the property as a nice house with a nice basement area as well. She also produced photographs for us.

COMMENT

We consider that the sort of organisation run by John Vanner has a role to play in housing mentally ill people, and we agree with him that at a basic level such an organisation provides a base for care in the community. However it cannot stand alone.

30.0. GENERAL PRACTITIONER INVOLVEMENT   DR PATEL

30.1. 23 SEPTEMBER 1992 TO 22 OCTOBER 1992

30.1.1. Christopher Clunis applied to join Dr Patel's list on 23 September 1992. We have heard evidence from Dr Anant Patel. At the initial visit a nurse at the practice noted down a certain amount of basic information, but Dr Patel did not see him. He visited again on 29 September 1992 when he was seen by Dr Patel's partner, Dr Paun, and asked for his NHS medical card. Dr Paun advised Christopher Clunis to telephone the Family Health Services Authority to obtain his card.

30.1.2. Dr Patel saw Christopher Clunis in the surgery on 7 October 1992 when he attended asking for a sickness certificate which he wanted to be backdated to August 1992 so that he could claim benefits. Dr Patel told him that he would provide a certificate for the period since he had been registered with Dr Patel, from 23 September 1992 but that he could not backdate it further. We were told that Christopher Clunis was then abusive and threatened Dr Patel and tried to hit him. Dr Patel pushed the "panic button" and his receptionist came into the room, stood between them and calmed Christopher Clunis down. Dr Patel then wrote him a certificate for four weeks from 7 October 1992. He prescribed treatment on the basis of what the patient had told the practice previously. Christopher Clunis then left the surgery.

30.1.3. Dr Patel wrote no note about the incident in the patient's notes. He told us his reason for not so doing: "We never make any derogatory remarks in the notes because that is harmful to the patient" but he accepted that he would wish to know if a patient he was taking on had a history of violence. He told us that it might be difficult to write about such an incident in the notes because a patient now has the right to access to his notes under the Access to Health Records Act 1990 unless disclosure would be likely to cause "serious harm to the physical or mental health of the patient." On the following day, 8 October 1992, Dr Patel wrote to the Family Health Services Authority asking that Christopher Clunis be removed from his list. On 20 October 1992 Christopher Clunis again attended the surgery demanding to know why he had been removed from Dr Patel's list. Dr Patel spoke to him briefly and the patient left "in anger". That was the last time Dr Patel saw Christopher Clunis and he was removed from Dr Patel's list on 22 October 1992.

30.1.4. On receipt of Dr Patel's letter, the Family Health Services Authority wrote to Christopher Clunis telling him that his name was to be removed from Dr Patel's list on 22nd October 1992. Unfortunately a list of other General Practitioners in the area was omitted from the letter sent to Christopher Clunis. We have heard evidence from Miss Hilary Scott, General Manager of Enfield and Haringey Family Health Services Authority. We understand that lists are now always sent to patients with letters telling them they have been removed from a G.P.'s list and that the form of such letters is being amended. We would recommend that the simpler such a letter can be, the better.

COMMENT

We are very concerned that a General Practitioner is able to remove a patient from his list, without any communication to anyone other than the Family Health Services Authority. Where the patient may well be psychiatrically ill and in need of prompt care and treatment, this means that less care is likely to be provided when more is in fact needed.

31.0. FRIERN HOSPITAL

30.0.1. In 1992 Friern Hospital was a Psychiatric Hospital providing both general and forensic psychiatric services. Friern Hospital provided in patient beds for Hampstead, Bloomsbury, Islington and West Haringey districts but in respect of patients from West Haringey provided out patient care as well. There was a clear demarcation line setting out the relevant catchment area for Friern Hospital and its neighbour, Chase Farm Hospital. Friern Hospital was closed in March 1993.

30.0.2. We heard evidence from Dr Janet Seargeant, Associate Specialist in General Psychiatry. Part of her job was to work in the out-patient department at Friern Hospital under 3 different Consultants, one of whom was Dr Sarah Taylor. We also heard evidence from Dr Taylor who is a part time Locum Consultant Psychiatrist. Dr Henry Kennedy was the Consultant Forensic Psychiatrist at Friern Hospital. We also heard evidence from him. In addition we heard evidence from Miss Nancy Korman, General Manager of Mental Health Services for Haringey.

31.1. FRIERN HOSPITAL INVOLVEMENT

9 OCTOBER 1992 TO 13 NOVEMBER 1992

31.1.1. Christopher Clunis failed to attend the out patient appointment at Friern Hospital on 9 October 1992, which had been made for him by Dr Gupta. Dr Seargeant thought that two S 117 Mental Health Act forms had been received at Friern Hospital by 9 October 1992 although she had not seen them by that date. He was sent another appointment for 6 November 1992 which was later changed to 13 November 1992. Dr Seargeant received various documents from Dr Gupta on 9 November 1992, namely the Kneesworth admission summary, court report and a letter of transfer to Guy's, and a discharge summary signed by Dr Gupta and Dr McCarthy. She was sure these documents did not arrive until just before the appointment for 13 November 1992. It is clear from the evidence we have heard from Dr Gupta and Dr McCarthy that she was right. She looked at the patient's file and then discovered the two S.117 Mental Health Act forms in the file. She was astounded to see herself named as the keyworker when she had never agreed to take over that role, not least because in her view it is a role generally taken by a social worker or community nurse. She did not ring Dr Gupta to ask for an explanation. She was critical of the lack of information on the forms.

31.1.2. Christopher Clunis did not attend the appointment on 13 November 1992 either. Dr Taylor had arranged to see Christopher Clunis herself on that day. Dr Seargeant spoke to Dr Taylor about the matter and agreed to make some enquiries. Dr Taylor knew Dr Seargeant well and was happy to leave matters in her hands. Dr Seargeant telephoned the General Practitioner, Dr Patel, and discovered that Christopher Clunis had been removed from his list because of his aggressive behaviour. She then telephoned social services who said that they had not been in touch with him because they had been told by the social worker at Guy's Hospital that he did not need any social work involvement. Dr Seargeant considered that a Mental Health Assessment Team should be set up to visit Christopher Clunis and asked Social Services to arrange a Team visit. Dr Seargeant also rang Dr Gupta to see if Christopher Clunis had been seen at Guy's since his discharge. Dr Gupta said that he had not been to Guy's but advised Dr Seargeant to ask the police to attend the Mental Health Assessment Team visit. The date of the 30th November 1992 was fixed for the visit. Dr Seargeant told us that in her view a planned assessment was required, not an urgent assesment.

COMMENT

We consider that the Mental Health Assessment Team visit should have been arranged more quickly, and that Dr Seargeant should have ensured that an earlier date was fixed.

32.0. HARINGEY HOUSING EMERGENCY GROUP

32.1. OCTOBER TO DECEMBER 1992

32.1.1. On 19 October 1992 Kieran Gillan telephoned John Vanner to find out how Christopher Clunis was. He said that someone from the Maidstone Property Group went to 112 Marlborough Road every other day and that both Christopher Clunis and the flat were fine. "He is looking after himself and the accommodation well."

32.1.2. Christopher Clunis did not attend the Housing Emergency Group appointment on 26 October 1992 although he did call on the following day, unbeknown to Kieran Gillan, about his rent. He also called in on 19 November 1992 bringing a letter from the DSS regarding his benefits. Once again Kieran Gillan was unaware of that visit. Kieran Gillan had in the meantime sought the assistance of John Vanner in asking Christopher Clunis to contact him. Christopher Clunis telephoned Kieran Gillan and another appointment was arranged for 4 December 1992. Kieran Gillan did not make a record of that telephone call although he is clear that it took place because it was the only time he ever spoke to Christopher Clunis. Christopher Clunis attended that appointment although Kieran Gillan could not and he was seen by another member of the Group. The duty manager at the Housing Emergency Group then gave authority to Christopher Clunis to extend his stay at 112 Marlborough Road. He was given a further appointment for 18 December 1992 to see Kieran Gillan. He did not attend that appointment because by then he was in custody.

33.0. G.P. INVOLVEMENT DR SIVANANTHAN

33.1. 29 OCTOBER 1992

33.1.1. Christopher Clunis applied to join Dr Sivananthan's list on 29 October 1992 and he was seen by Dr Sivananthan on that day. We heard evidence from Dr Nalliah Sivananthan. Christopher Clunis told Dr Sivananthan that he was a schizophrenic, that he had an outpatient's appointment at Friern Hospital on the 13 November 1992 and that he wanted a medical certificate and a prescription for chlorpromazine. He said he had recently been in Guy's Hospital. Dr Sivanthan said he had a nice discussion with Christopher Clunis and that he felt sorry for him. He was satisfied that he would be getting help when he attended Friern Hospital for his appointment and he did not feel it was necessary for him to take any further steps. Christopher Clunis was seen by the practice nurse before he left the surgery for a routine check. That was the first and only time that Dr Sivananthan saw Christopher Clunis. He had no records, save his own, relating to Christopher Clunis, and never received any.

34.0. HARINGEY SOCIAL SERVICES

34.1. THE ADVICE AND ASSESSMENT TEAM

34.1.1. In July 1992 the Wood Green Office of Haringey Social Services was restructured into an Advice and Assessment Team, a Learning Difficulties Team, a Children and Families Team and an Elderly and Disabled Team. The specialist Mental Health Team was situated at the Hornsey Office. The Advice and Assessment Team acted as the duty front line team which received all new work, and after assessment, referred clients on to the other teams when necessary. The Advice and Assessment Team was supposed to consist of 8 social workers and two managers but it was considerably understaffed (mostly operating at half strength) and the social workers were all newly qualified and inexperienced. In consequence there was a heavy reliance on the advice and experience of the two Team Leaders, or Managers as they were subsequently called. One of the Team Leaders became ill and was off work for 8 months. An Team Manager appointed from an agency tried to fill in as Team Leader on a half time basis but could not cope. Mr Peter Townley, who had some previous experience as a Team Leader in Haringey, was appointed as a temporary replacement in October 1992. Then the second Team Leader was ill for 2 weeks at the beginning of December 1992. There was no real continuity, and we were told that sometimes there was no team leader at all. No member of the Team was an Approved Social Worker. The Team found itself under considerable pressure because of the volume of work and the shortage of staff. Its members made many complaints to management about the perceived problems but they say little action was taken.

34.1.2. We have heard evidence from Mrs Joan Lawrence, Team Manager for the Advice and Assessment Team, Mr Peter Townley, Temporary Team Manager of the Advice and Assessment Team, and Mr Brian Payne, District Service Manager at Wood Green Office of Haringey Social Services department.

34.1.3. Joan Lawrence told us that she was appointed as a full time Team Leader of the newly created Advice and Assessment Team in July 1992. The other Team Leader was Nona Getty but she became ill in August 1992 and was off work for about 8 months. Joan Lawrence tried to carry on, on her own, and then Peter Townley was employed temporarily to help her. She voiced her anxiety to Brian Payne that the team she was leading was under strength. He suggested recruiting agency staff and such staff were recruited. She found herself running a team made up entirely of newly qualified or agency staff which increased her workload immeasurably. She told us that she worked alternate weeks as Duty Team Leader for new referrals so that the other Team Leader was supposed to cover those weeks when she was not fulfilling that role.

34.1.4. Joan Lawrence told us that she was unwell herself and away from work between 30 November and 12 December 1992. She returned to work on Monday 14 December 1992. She was not duty Team Leader that week.

34.1.5. Peter Townley told us that he was appointed to the Advice and Assessment Team on 23 October 1992. Prior to his involvement another Team Leader from another Team had been asked to cover the Advice and Assessment Team on a half time basis. Perhaps not surprisingly that had not worked so that Peter Townley was then appointed. Then, when Joan Lawrence became ill, he could not, on his own, provide all the supervision and support that was necessary. He thought that in fact he had little contact with the Christopher Clunis case.

34.1.6. We have been unable to ascertain whether one or two files were created for Christopher Clunis. Some witnesses told us that there was only one file and that it contained all the information relating to Christopher Clunis, others told us that when they looked at the file the handwritten notes relating to his assessment by Julian Green at Kneesworth House were not included. Certainly there is a note dated 28 April 1993 on the one now existing file which reads: "During allocation on 27 April 1993 another file on Mr Clunnis was discovered". There is no ready explanation for this since Christopher Clunis was always referred under the same name which he was using at that time, namely Christopher Clunis.

COMMENT

In our view the Advice and Assessment Team was a change in structure which did not not work in the period we have investigated. It was understaffed from its inception in July 1992, and its members were recently qualified social workers or temporary workers from employment agencies. It would have required expert and consistent operational management, but this was disrupted from August 1992 when one of the Team Leaders went on long term sick leave. In consequence we find that from October 1992 social workers only received occasional individual supervision to review their caseloads about every six weeks, instead of every fortnight.

Despite these huge shortcomings the team was still expected to fulfil its original functions; to receive all new referrals to the Wood Green Office, to provide appropriate advice, to make full assessments, to handle immediate needs, to pass on clients to specialised and long term Teams only when assessment and initial work had been completed. For this reason it was possible for clients to be passed from one social worker to another in the team depending upon who was on duty. One of the Social Workers on the Team, Maria Anastasi, told us that it was common for four or five social workers to have a hand in an individual case, each having to pick up the threads from others' notes and recollections. We observe that this occurred in Christopher Clunis' case.

We are told that the Advice and Assessment Team is still in place although it is now better resourced. However Nancy Korman, General Manager of hatringey Mental health Services, told us that she remains very unhappy with the present form of the Team. She has told Haringey Social Services that the Health Services would like new referrals to go to the specialist Mental Health Team, who are skilled in assessing patients and have a good working relationship with the Mental Health Services. She has collected views and put them to the Social Services department and asked them to reconsider the system.

At a late stage in the Inquiry we were sent anonymously a copy of a letter dated 25 February 1993 signed by several Social Workers in the Advice and Assessment Team to management asking for the whole system to be reconsidered. The anonymous note said that nothing had come of that letter.

We are not impressed by anonymous communications, but we do feel it supports our view that the Team was not properly structured, staffed or supervised.

HARINGEY SOCIAL SERVICES' CONTACT WITH CHRISTOPHER CLUNIS

34.1.7. We have already described the circumstances in which Haringey Social Services were involved in making the S.3 Mental Health Act 1983 assessment on Christopher Clunis at Kneesworth House on 20 August 1992. Julian Green had gone to visit him and had made a recommendation for his detention in hospital. Haringey Social Services were not subsequently informed that Christopher Clunis was being transferred to Guy's Hospital and Julian Green had no further contact with the case. When he was discharged from Guy's Hospital no one from the Social Services department was asked to attend the S 117 Mental Health Act 1983 meeting.

34.2. COMMUNICATION FROM GUY'S HOSPITAL – 28 SEPTEMBER 1992

34.2.1. On 28 September 1992 the Wood Green office of Haringey Social Services received a letter from Anne Witham, Social Worker from Guy's Hospital about Christopher Clunis. The letter said he was "subject to S.117 aftercare and has been rehoused in your area"; that he suffered from schizophrenia and had been detained under S. 3 of the Mental Health Act since May 1992 after he had seriously injured another resident at a hostel when he was unwell; that "he is quite capable of self care and should be able to cope well with independent living"; that he had an outpatient appointment at Friern Hospital, and concluded: "I do not feel that there is a need for any social work intervention with Mr Clunnis at present...". That letter was placed in a file and no action was taken.

34.3. REFERRAL FROM FRIERN HOSPITAL – 13 NOVEMBER 1992

34.3.1. On Friday 13 November 1992 Mrs Joan Lawrence, Team Leader in the Advice and Assessment Team, received a telephone call from Dr Seargeant of Friern Hospital about Christopher Clunis telling her that he was the subject of S.117 Mental Health Act 1983 aftercare, that he had failed to attend two outpatient appointments at Friern, and that he had been struck off his General Practitioner's list because his manner was very threatening. Dr Seargeant asked for a Mental Health Assessment to be set up with a S.12 approved Doctor and with the police in attendance.

34.3.2. On Tuesday 17 November 1992 Dr Seargeant telephoned the Wood Green Office again and spoke to Miss Janine Lewis to find out whether an Assessment had been organised. We have heard evidence from Janine Lewis. She had qualified as a Social Worker in July 1991 and began to work for Haringey Social Services in August 1992. She was uncertain whether Christopher Clunis was living at number 5 or number 112 Marlborough Road. Janine Lewis told us that she rang the Emergency Housing Group in Haringey to find out his correct address. She was told that they had no knowledge of Christopher Clunis. In fact he was known to the Housing Emergency Group and they had provided accommodation for him. They had seen him on at least 3 occasions by that time and we have been unable to find out how or why the incorrect information was given to Janine Lewis. Christopher Clunis had been given a computer number within the Housing Emergency Group and no explanation could be given for how they professed not to know him. We accept however what Janine Lewis told us. We found her an honest, caring and concerned person and we have no doubt she contacted the Housing Emergency Group to find out whether they knew of Christopher Clunis. Kieran Gillan, who worked at the Housing Emergency Group, told us that the system within the Housing Emergency Group has been known to fall down before and therefore he was concerned but not surprised by the failure of the Group to identify Christopher Clunis as their client.

34.3.3. Janine Lewis tried to check with his former General Practitioner. Later that day Dr Seargeant said she would contact Guy's to find out the correct address and suggested that 30 November 1992 at 3.00 pm would be a suitable date and time for the proposed Mental Health Assessment. Janine Lewis was quite clear that the suggested appointment was made by Dr Seargeant because it was not her role to do that, and she said, "I would have had to consult other people as well". As we have already stated Dr Seargeant did not consider that an urgent assessment was needed.

34.3.4. On 18 November 1992 Janine Lewis contacted the General Practitioner surgery and discovered that Christopher Clunis' address was in fact 112 Marlborough Road. Janine Lewis told the Team Leader of her action and the matter was then passed on to Chris Diakou. On 20 November 1992 Chris Diakou asked Ms Carole Jennings, an Approved Social Worker, whether she could attend the assessment on 30 November 1992 and she agreed to do so. On the same day Chris Diakou also tried to contact Dr Mullen, a Doctor approved under S.12 Mental Health Act and left a message. Carole Jennings then took over the matter. We have heard evidence from her. She is an Approved Social Worker who had spent 6 months in a psychotherapeutic community but otherwise her experience of patients suffering from mental illness was limited.

34.3.5. Carole Jennings rang Dr Mullen twice on 26 November 1992 and when she finally spoke to him he said he could not make 3.00pm but would be able to attend at 4.30 pm on 30 November 1992. She then tried to speak to Dr Seargeant but she was unavailable. Carole Jennings eventually spoke to Dr Seargeant on 27 November 1992 when the latter told her something of Christopher Clunis' violent history and said that she could attend at 4.30pm on 30 November 1992 for the Mental Health Assessment. Carole Jennings and Janine Lewis told us that neither Julian Green's notes nor the Guy's Hospital S.117 aftercare forms were on the file, nor could Carole Jennings recall seeing the Guy's Hospital letter from Anne Witham. She subsequently rang Guy's Social work department to find out the name and address of his next of kin but was told that they had no record.

34.4. THE ATTEMPTED MENTAL HEALTH ASSESSMENT – 30 NOVEMBER 1992

34.4.1. The date for the visit was fixed for 30 November 1992. Dr Seargeant felt that the date had been dictated to a certain extent by the need for Social Services to make enquiries. However the social worker involved (Janine Lewis) was quite clear that the date had been suggested by Dr Seargeant. We accept that the date was suggested by Dr Seargeant; certainly she made no objection to that date.

34.4.2. On 30 November 1992 Dr Seargeant rang Carole Jennings and once again queried Christopher Clunis' address. Carole Jennings rang his former General Practitioner and was told that the address was 112 Marlborough Road. That was the second time that Social Services had taken that step. She asked the police and ambulance to attend the Assessment.

34.4.3. It was a dark and wet evening. The ambulance and police were already there when Carole Jennings, Janine Lewis and Dr Seargeant arrived. The ambulance men told them that a man had just left the premises. Dr Mullen was late. While they were all waiting for Dr Mullen a man returned to the address and then came out again wearing a hat and coat. No member of the team knew what Christopher Clunis looked like save that he was black. They had no idea whether the man leaving the property was he or not. They did not stop him. Eventually Dr Mullen arrived. There was no answer when the Assessment Team knocked at the premises so that no assessment was done. In fact the man who had been seen leaving the premises was Christopher Clunis. Carole Jennings left a card at the property asking him to call into the Wood Green Office of Haringey Social Services on the following day and Dr Seargeant also wrote him a letter asking him to go to Friern Hospital.

34.4.4. Dr Seargeant told us that she had spoken to the police and they had asked her how long ago the person they were trying to assess had been considered dangerous. She told them, and they then indicated that their presence might not be necessary if there were no recent complaints of violence. She said they were perfectly polite but she got the impression that they did not want to be asked to attend unless the man had been violent in the recent past.

34.4.5. We have heard evidence from PC Neville Sullivan who was one of the Officers who attended with the Mental Health Assessment Team that evening. He is an Officer in the Winchmore Hill Satellite Station which comes under the main Police Station at Edmonton, Fore Street, London N9. He could not recall a great deal about the visit. He remembered that he and another officer went in a Police car to Marlborough Road where two ladies, whom he thought were social workers, came to talk to him. He could not recall where in Marlborough Road they had been directed and thought that no number might have been given. They asked them to remain in the car while they went to the house and said they would call if they needed help. PC Sullivan said that as is usual in such cases they adopted a very low profile because they did not wish to upset a person who might be mentally ill. PC Sullivan's impression was that a police presence was required in order to protect the Social Workers if necessary. He could not remember talking to a doctor nor whether his colleague had done so. He felt it was unlikely that he would have suggested to the doctor that police presence was not really necessary because he feels it is important for female social workers to be safe. He said he had no idea what the man looked like whom the Team were trying to assess.

34.4.6. Superintendent Barker told us that she had spoken to the other officer who attended the Mental Health Assessment visit. She identified him as PC Gambrill. He told her they were directed to go to 112 Marlborough Road where they met 2 social workers. He did not believe that an ambulance was present.

34.4.7. We asked Dr Seargeant why a second assessment visit was not arranged. She said that option had been considered but it was decided, "to try once again getting his goodwill and getting to see him informally, and so we thought that we would try that first and proceed to the next step if that didn't work." She did not discuss the matter further with Dr Taylor, Consultant Psychiatrist.

COMMENT

We repeat that the gap between the first request for a Mental Health Assessment on 13 November 1992 and the visit that was arranged for 30 November 1992 was in our view far too long. We also consider that there was plenty of time to prepare preliminary information about Christopher Clunis so that alternative responses following his assessment could be planned.

We note, in passing, that is does seem to be potentially wasteful of time and effort if a Mental Health Assessment visit is made, when no member of the Team can identify the patient.

34.5. VISIT TO THE OFFICE – 1 DECEMBER 1992

34.5.1. On 1 December 1992 Christopher Clunis went to the Wood Green office of Haringey Social Services. Janine Lewis told us that she rang Dr Seargeant and told her that he had come into the Office and Dr Seargeant gave her an outpatient appointment to give him. He was seen subsequently by Carole Jennings and Janine Lewis and he agreed to attend the new appointment at Friern Hospital on 10 December 1992. Carole Jennings conducted the interview and she asked him why he had not attended the earlier appointments at Friern. He apparently replied that he was not receiving his benefits, by which she understood him to mean that he had no money to attend the Hospital. He was then asked about the fact that he did not have a General Practitioner. He said he had a new one but he could not remember his name or address. She asked him whether he had any family and he replied that he did not. Carole Jennings knew that was incorrect because she had been told by the Guy's Hospital Social Worker that he had a sister in the area. Otherwise she thought there was nothing untoward in his attitude or behaviour. Janine Lewis did not feel he was evasive in any way or agitated or subdued but she did feel he was wary during the interview. However she had no real misgivings about him or his behaviour on that day. She agreed to help him with his benefits. No formal discussion took place between the social workers after the visit, and Janine Lewis wrote a note about the visit which Carole Jennings did not see. Mr Peter Townley, Temporary Team Leader, told us that, having worked with Carole Jennings for some time within the department, she was cautious and he would be guided by her assessment of a client's mental health. Hence on 1 December 1992 he relied on the assessment made of Christopher

Clunis and he was content that a further out patient appointment had been arranged. He said there was nothing that rang warning bells with him at that time.

34.5.2. Dr Seargeant told us that it was her recollection that the social workers had telephoned her in Christopher Clunis' presence and that they had indicated he was reasonably friendly, had sought their help on benefits and money, and that in their view there was no immediate cause for concern. Dr Seargeant therefore made him a new outpatient appointment which the social workers passed on to Christopher Clunis. She spoke to Janine Lewis, not to Carole Jennings, the Approved Social Worker. Dr Seargeant asked that an Approved Social Worker attend the new out patient appointment.

COMMENT

There is a discrepancy between the recollection of Dr Seargeant on the one hand and the recollections of Carole Jennings and Janine Lewis on the other. The Social Workers said that the discussion with Dr Seargeant took place before they interviewed Christopher Clunis. The note of the telephone call appears before the note of the interview in the records. Dr Seargeant however told us that they rang her during the course of the interview and that she was reassured when they told her he appeared fine. We do not consider it necessary to make a finding on this point particularly as Dr Seargeant now tells us that she cannot remember exactly when she received this information.

The interview could provide only a snapshot of Christopher Clunis. We note that the two social workers were reassured as others had been before them. Christopher Clunis had the ability to achieve this effect with people who were not fully aware of his history or could not observe him over a period of time.

34.6 2 DECEMBER 1992 TO 11 DECEMBER 1992

34.6.1. On 2 December 1992 Janine Lewis set out a course of recommended action namely: (i) to find out who was Christopher Clunis' new General Practitioner – on 4 December 1992 the Family Health Services Authority said that his records had not yet been received by them and would not be until he had re-registered with a new general practitioner; (ii) to contact the DSS regarding his benefits – Janine Lewis telephoned the DSS on 11 December 1992 who told her that as far as they were concerned there were no problems with him receiving benefits; (iii) to discuss with Dr Seargeant that it was Social Services' view that an Approved Social Worker need not attend the outpatient appointment on 10 December 1992 but that a duty worker should attend to make an assessment of his social needs – Dr Seargeant agreed.

34.7. THE OUTPATIENT APPOINTMENT – 10 DECEMBER 1992

34.7.1. Christopher Clunis failed to attend the appointment fixed at Friern hospital for 10 December 1992. Miss Sarah Bartlett attended that appointment from Wood Green Social Services. She was a temporary agency worker. We have not heard evidence from her since she no longer works for social services and is now living in New Zealand. She discussed the way forward with Dr Seargeant. Dr Seargeant told us that the alternatives were another Mental Health Assessment visit or an attempt to get him to visit the social services department again and then giving him another outpatient appointment. Dr Taylor, the Locum Consultant at Friern Hospital, told us that Dr Seargeant did not raise the matter with her. Sarah Bartlett discussed matters with the

Team Leader. Peter Townley told us that he was not the duty Team Leader on that day and that Joan Lawrence was away on sick leave. He thought he might have popped in to help (in the midst of his other duties) but he could not recall talking to Sarah Bartlett about the matter. Sarah Bartlett's note states that it was decided that the Social Workers would visit Christopher Clunis at home taking a vodaphone with them. They would speak to him on the doorstep and visit at a time when Naveed Bokhari (who was one of the Advice and Assessment Team and had recently completed Approved Social Worker training) could attend. In fact this did not happen. We were told that on 11 December 1992 Janine Lewis wrote to Christopher Clunis asking him to attend an appointment at the Wood Green office on 24 December 1992 and she informed Dr Seargeant of that. Dr Seargeant was told of this date and was told it was the earliest date they could give. She said to us, "I felt that it was a pity that it was so far in advance but I felt that at that point we had made an arrangement so it should be within social services' hands because the only alternative would be to go out and do a full assessment." She did not discuss the matter with Dr Taylor, the Consultant Psychiatrist.

34.7.2. Janine Lewis was not on duty on 10 December 1992 but recalls being told by Sarah Bartlett that an appointment needed to be made for when Miss Bokhari was back. She believes that she would have been told on 11 December 1992 by the Team Leader to make an appointment for Christopher Clunis to visit the office. If she misunderstood her instructions she said that this should have been picked up by the Team Leader at the end of the day. It was not. We have not been able to identify which Team Leader was on duty on that day.

COMMENT

Indecision and procrastination is the hall mark of the failure of Haringey Social Services to have any responsible person making decisions and monitoring decisions that had been made. Equally Dr Seargeant left too much to the Social Services department when she should have been taking an active role. She did not involve her Consultant, Dr Taylor, in managing this difficult case. As the person named as keyworker under the S 117 Mental Health Act 1983 aftercare plan, Dr Seargeant knew that if she did not do so, no one else would.

35.0 VIOLENT INCIDENTS INVOLVING MEMBERS OF THE PUBLIC AND THE POLICE

35.1. FIRST INCIDENT – WEDNESDAY 9 DECEMBER 1992

35.1.1. We heard evidence from Mr Nigel Bartlett. He is a tall man, 6 feet 4 inches in height and of sturdy build. We found him a most impressive witness, calm, honest and with a clear recollection of the events which he described graphically to us.

35.1.2. He told us that he had been out during the evening of 9 December 1992, walking from Palmers Green to Wood Green in North London. He became aware of a man ahead of him who was shouting at some people on the other side of the road. Mr Bartlett walked down the road and then realised that the same man was walking behind him in Belsize Road. He quickened his pace and walked into the road but the man, who was ranting and raving, followed him and began running. The man passed him and then turned round to face Mr Bartlett, who continued walking so that the man was now walking backwards in front of him. The man spoke to Mr Bartlett and said, "Are you the devil?" Mr Bartlett was very concerned but made no reply. The man asked him if he was happy and Mr Bartlett said "no". Mr Bartlett then noticed that the man had something in his hand which shone in the street light. He thought it was a knife. He described the man as being slightly smaller than himself but with a heavy rotund build, "like the Michelin man". The man began to wave the object and Mr Bartlett realised he was holding a screwdriver. He told Mr Bartlett to take off his glasses which Mr Bartlett refused to do, and then the man hit Mr Bartlett with his fist (the one that was holding the screwdriver) and caught him on the nose near to his eye. Mr Bartlett fell to the ground to try and deflect the blow and began to yell in the hope that a resident would come out. The man slowly and calmly walked off. Mr Bartlett told us he was very frightened by the incident. We fully understood that.

35.1.3. Mr and Mrs Hislop who lived in Belsize Avenue heard Mr Bartlett's shouts and came to his aid. They took him into their house and called the police. They washed Mr Bartlett's wound, which he told us bled profusely although it was only a small cut. He said that in his view the wound had been caused by his glasses rather than by the screwdriver. He later discovered that his glasses had been chipped and part of the bridge had been broken.

35.1.4. The Police took some time to arrive and Mr and Mrs Hislop telephoned the police again. An Officer did eventually arrive (whom we have been able to identify as PC Sullivan), the delay having been caused because there was a change of shift. Mr Bartlett told us that he informed the Officer that he wanted to press charges, because he thought it might happen to someone else. However, according to Mr Bartlett, the Officer said that as the person sounded mentally ill, it was unlikely that the Crown Prosecution Service would wish to charge him. He also said that he had an idea who the man was and that he lived nearby. He told Mr Bartlett he could bring a civil action against the man but it would not be worthwhile if the man had no money. Mr Bartlett accepted that a person who is mentally ill is not responsible for his actions and decided not to pursue the matter. He was quite happy that no further step should be taken because of the man's probable psychiatric illness and because it was a relatively minor incident. The Officer kindly took him home.

35.1.5. We have received written evidence from Mrs Hislop. She had no doubt that the Officer who came to her house to see Mr Bartlett recognised the description of the man given by Mr Bartlett, and said that the man was known to the Police and lived in the area in Whittington Road. She and her husband were quite sure that on the evening of the attack the Officer told them that the Police had had previous contact with the man who attacked Mr Bartlett.

35.1.6. We have heard evidence from PC Neville Sullivan, the Officer who attended Mr Bartlett at Mr and Mrs Hislop's house in Belsize Avenue. He happens to be the same Officer who attended Christopher Clunis' address with the Mental Health Assessment Team on 30 November 1992.

35.1.7. After giving evidence to us, PC Sullivan produced a Crime/Arrest Investigation Report (called a crime sheet) for us, completed by him on 9 December 1992. From that report it is clear that the first telephone call was received at 9.30 pm and that PC Sullivan arrived at the Hislop's house at 10.10 pm. He took a short statement from

Mr Bartlett and recorded that Mr Bartlett had been punched once in the face causing a small 2 inch cut below the eye which he felt did not require stitches. He recorded that the assailant had told Mr Bartlett to take off his glasses, and initially wrote down that a screwdriver had been used but then crossed that out and wrote that the blow was made with a fist. The fact that he had written the word 'screwdriver' on the crime sheet is of particular importance to the narrative. No action was taken other than information being sent to statistics branch and the record being filed in storage on 18 December 1992.

35.1.8. PC Sullivan told us that a number of Officers went to the scene to look for the suspect, but that he went to Mr and Mrs Hislop's house. He could not recall whether he had seen Mr Bartlett in the Street or in the Hislop's house although it is clear from the Crime Sheet that the victim had run into Mr and Mrs Hislop's house before he arrived. He had not seen the Crime Sheet when he gave evidence to us and to the extent that his evidence is at variance with the Crime Sheet we accept what he wrote on the sheet on the day as being more likely to be accurate than his recollection over a year later. He considered that the offence described by Mr Bartlett was common assault and he told us that it is the victim himself who tends to determine what action is taken. He recalled the description of the assailant as a very large black man and the crime sheet described the suspect as 6 feet 3 inches, Afro-Carribean, and very large. PC Sullivan could not recall that Mr Bartlett had mentioned a screwdriver to him and thought that Mr Bartlett may have picked this up afterwards from a newspaper report after the murder of Jonathan Zito. PC Sullivan told us he circulated details of the assailant to the Police so that they could search the area.

35.1.9. PC Sullivan denied that he had told Mr Bartlett that he knew who the assailant was. He told us he had no idea who the assailant was. He told us that he did not recall Mr Bartlett referring to the word 'devil' when describing the attack. PC Sullivan then gave this evidence, "I didn't know that the man who had done this assault was a mental patient to start with, and I didn't know that the man we went round to in Whittington Road was a Mr Clunis. I hadn't seen him. They didn't give me a picture. . . ."

35.1.10. Sergeant Staples also gave evidence to us. He is based at Area Headquarters, Edmonton. He told us that Marlborough Road is divided for policing into Edmonton Division for part of the road, and Hornsey Division for the other part.

35.1.11. COMMENT

35.1.12. *We find it of considerable significance that the crime sheet does refer to a screwdriver, although that word had subsequently been crossed out. We find it difficult to accept that PC Sullivan did not know the assailant was a mental patient since from the story told him by Mr Bartlett it was fairly obvious that the attacker was mentally disturbed. Secondly, both Mr Bartlett and Mrs Hislop clearly recall the Officer saying that the man was mentally unstable. Thirdly PC Sullivan told Mrs Hislop (according to her) that the Police knew the attacker lived in Whittington Road. In fact Christopher Clunis lived in Marlborough Road, but PC Sullivan in his evidence to us said that he had gone with the Mental Health Assessment Team to a man "who lived in Whittington Road". Fourthly the word 'devil' was subsequently referred to by Inspector Gill in a message to Haringey Social Services. To the extent that the versions of what took place on 9 December 1992 given to us by Mr Bartlett and Mrs Hislop on the one hand, and given to us by PC Sullivan on the other, vary, we have no hesitation in accepting that what we were told by Mr Bartlett and Mrs Hislop is correct.*

35.2. SECOND INCIDENT – WEDNESDAY 9 DECEMBER 1992

35.2.1. We heard evidence from Mrs Susan Parashar who lives in Whittington Road London. At 9.35 pm on 9 December 1992 she took her 2 dogs out for a walk. She met her son and some of his friends. She described an enormous black man approaching them who tried to join in the conversation. She did not find him menacing but he was incoherent. The man went to touch one of her dogs but the dog growled and barked and the man became annoyed. Mrs Parashar went off for her walk and she could hear the man shouting abuse at her.

35.2.2. Subsequently she was told by her son that the man had then got out a screwdriver and began chasing him and his friends around the parked cars in the street. One of the boys went to a telephone box outside the off licence and rang for the Police. In the meantime we were told by Superintendent Barker that the man went into the Albion Off Licence run by a Greek couple and was rude to a young couple who were in the shop. The owner asked him to leave which he did and then rang the Police. The owner and his wife recognised the man; he had been in their shop before and had previously made somewhat offensive remarks.

35.2.3. We were told by Mrs Parashar that Christopher Clunis then began to threaten the boy who was still in the telephone box trying to call the police. So her son and his friends called to the man and were able to divert his attention from the young man in the kiosk. The man then began chasing them again with the screwdriver all around the cars that were parked in the street. Then he appeared to give up, walked down Marlborough Road and into one of the houses.

35.2.4. Mrs Parashar's son came to look for her because he was worried about her, but he found her after a short while in her home. He then went off again to wait for the police who had not as yet arrived. Mrs Parashar herself then telephoned the police who said they had the matter in hand. Shortly afterwards Mrs Parashar answered the telephone to a woman who said she was from Edmonton Police station and asked for a description of the man. She then said "I think we know who that is". The police eventually arrived and she told them what had happened, although neither she, nor her son, nor any of his friends were asked to give a statement.

35.2.5. Superintendent Barker told us that messages were recorded on a Computer Aided Despatch (CAD), but that a link between connecting events has to be made by the operator. At that time CAD messages were only kept for 6 months, so that by the time Superintendent Barker came to investigate matters the messages had been destroyed. She was however able to find some, although not all, in relation to the incidents on 9 December 1992 and certainly it appeared that some link had been made between some of the incidents, but again not between all. She said that communication was made more difficult because different police stations dealt with different areas and sometimes those boundaries were not obvious. Part of a road would be covered by one station and the other part of the road by another station.

35.2.6. She also told us that 2 police officers from Edmonton searched the area in a car but could not find any trace of the assailant. Two other officers searched the area later but again found no trace of the assailant. It seems unlikely that the various incidents were linked by the Controller at Edmonton Police Station.

35.3. THURSDAY 10 DECEMBER 1992

35.3.1. On 10 December 1992 Mrs Parashar told us that one of her son's friends had seen the man in the street again and had followed him to his address in Marlborough Road and had remembered the number. He and her son and another friend had then gone to Wood Green Police Station to tell them the address of the man who had been chasing and threatening them the day before. Superintendent Barker told us that they gave the information to a Woman Police Officer. That officer recalls them coming in and telling her the address which she passed on to Edmonton Police Station. She could not now recall the number or whether they had given her a number. Her message would have been put on a CAD message but Superintendent Barker has not been able to find it.

35.3.2. Mrs Parashar said that she understood that the Police were not interested and said that it was a matter for Edmonton Police Station. Her son and his friends were rather upset at this response and so Mrs Parashar asked them to give her the address and she would contact Edmonton Police Station.

35.3.3. She did so at about 10.45 pm that evening. She rang Edmonton Police Station and spoke to the same woman she had spoken to on the previous evening. Mrs Parashar told her the address where the attacker lived. The gist of the reply was that they knew where he lived because they had attended there the previous week with an ambulance, psychiatrists, nurses and policemen but that he had not answered the door. She said they could not just go and arrest him, but advised that if Mrs Parashar saw him on the street she should telephone the police. Mrs Parashar felt that was very unsatisfactory, not least because the police had taken so long to attend the scene on 9 December 1992. So on the following day she contacted her friend Mrs Angela Esposito who is a Justice of the Peace to ask for her help.

35.4. FRIDAY 11 DECEMBER 1992

35.4.1. Inspector Delahay came on duty the following morning, 11 December 1992. He found a message waiting for him asking him to ring Mrs Esposito. He did so and was put in touch with Mrs Parashar. Through her he spoke to Mrs Parashar's son who could not, as far as Inspector Delahay can recall, remember the address of the assailant. Inspector Delahay told Superintendent Barker that at some stage, he cannot recall when or how, he realised there was a link between the police attendance on 30 November 1992 and the incidents on 9 December 1992. Since it was not in fact Inspector Delahay's sector he passed on the information to Inspector Gill of Winchmore Hill Police Station.

35.4.2. Friday 11 December 1992 to Monday 14 December 1992

35.4.3. We heard evidence from Mrs Esposito who lives in Palmers Green. She recalls speaking to Mrs Parashar and offered to ring Edmonton Police Station herself to speak to the Chief Superintendent. She in fact spoke to a number of policemen on that day and over the following weekend, including Inspector Delahay and Inspector Gill. She was trying to make them realise that a dangerous man was on the streets about whom members of the public were very worried and asking them do something about it. Apparently she kept being transferred from one station to another from Enfield to Edmonton, from Edmonton to Southgate, and from Southgate to Winchmore Hill. She became angry that the matter was being passed from pillar to post and said so. On Monday 14 December 1992 she recalls being telephoned by someone from the Social Services but she could not remember which department or exactly what was said during the telephone call. However at all times she made it abundantly clear that she and her friend were very worried that there was a dangerous man on the streets.

35.4.4. On Monday 14 December Mrs Parashar recalls being telephoned by Inspector Delahay from Edmonton who told her there was nothing to worry about and that the matter had been passed on to Inspector Gill at Winchmore Hill. Mrs Esposito recalls being rung by Inspector Gill on 15 December 1992 who told her that they had everything in hand. She insisted that he speak himself to Mrs Parashar because she felt Mrs Parashar deserved direct information. He did so and reassured Mrs Parashar. However her son's friend saw the man in the street again and tried to contact Inspector Gill, but had no success. Mrs Parashar remained very worried and did not know that the man was arrested for the murder of Jonathan Zito until the trial at the Old Bailey in June 1993. She did not know his name until that time either.

35.4.5. We have heard evidence from Inspector Derek Gill. He is an Inspector at Winchmore Hill Police Station, 687 Green Lanes, London N21. He told us he had been away for a long weekend and returned to duty on Monday 14 December 1992. He found waiting for him a message from Inspector Delahay who was Inspector for the Southgate sector. Inspector Delahay dealt with the matter on 12 December 1992 and left the message for Inspector Gill. No one looked at the message until Inspector Gill returned on Monday 14 December 1992. The message said that an incident had occurred on 9 December 1992 when a tall black man had been waving a knife at boys and in a mini cab office and that there might be a link with the visit to 112 Marlborough Road made by Officers on 30 December 1992 with some social workers. He also mentioned that Mrs Esposito had rung.

35.4.6. Inspector Gill telephoned Mrs Esposito and she told him that the person had waved a screwdriver at people and threatened them and he explained that the man could only be arrested for carrying an offensive weapon if he were in a public place.

35.5. COMMENT

35.5.1. *We are concerned at the lack of prompt response by the Police to these incidents, particularly when it was being dealt with at Inspector level. We do not find it impressive that a message was simply left in a tray to be picked up when the next Inspector happened to come on duty. There should have been much greater urgency in responding to public anxiety about Christopher Clunis' violent actions.*

35.5.2. *We are also concerned at the lack of communication between Police Divisions particularly in the circumstances that 2 or sometimes 3 divisions may be responsible for different parts of the same road. The Computer Aided Despatch system, as described to us, appears to be a hit and miss way of communicating between officers in different Divisions and sub Divisions, especially where communication is in any event made difficult by shift working and the complexity of boundaries.*

36.0. POLICE LIAISON WITH HARINGEY SOCIAL SERVICES

36.1. 15 – 16 DECEMBER 1992

36.1.1. According to Social Services records, on 15 December 1992 Inspector Gill rang the Wood Green Office and left a message. Carole Jennings found the message on her notepad in the afternoon and telephoned him. He told her that Christopher Clunis' neighbours had reported seeing him in the streets on 9 December 1992 waving screwdrivers and knives and talking about devils. She informed us that she was quite sure that the name Clunis was given to her by the Inspector. It seems that it would be unlikely that she would have been able to identify the man simply from his address, but even if she had done so, then she would have told the Inspector the man's name. She said she would report the matter to the duty worker and he said that he would not be available that day but he could be contacted the following day after 9.30 am and left his number. Carole Jennings immediately informed the duty worker, Mrs Maria Anastasi. She told Maria Anastasi that the message was in respect of Christopher Clunis and Maria Anastasi noted the message in his file. That was the end of Carole Jennings' involvement and she left the matter to the duty worker and the Advice and Assessment Team. That is her practice; she completes the task she is asked to do, as the Approved Social Worker, and then passes the matter back to the team that are supposed to be dealing with the case. She then has to return to her normal caseload on the Team caring for the Elderly and Adults with physical disabilities. She was not on duty again as the Approved Social Worker for another 4 to 6 weeks. She did not contact anyone else.

36.1.2. We heard evidence form Maria Anastasi. She had qualified in September 1992 and was part of the Advice and Assessment Team. She told us that Carole Jennings came down from her office to speak to her as the duty worker on that day. She recalled Carole Jennings giving her the message to telephone Inspector Gill about Christopher Clunis on the following day. She noted the matter in Christopher Clunis' file. We feel it is worth setting out her contemporaneous note:

> "Telephone Message from Inspector Gill 081 345****. Message left with Carole Jennings. Neighbours reported to Inspector Gill that Mr Clunis was seen in streets (9/12/92) waving screwdrivers and knives and talking about devils. Could we contact Inspector Gill tomorrow after 9.30." She signed that note and dated it 15 December 1992.

Inspector Gill told us that the telephone number was correctly recorded and was in fact his direct line.

36.1.3. Maria Anastasi told us that normally the matter would have been picked up at the end of the day by a Team Leader. It appears that Peter Townley was due to be Team Leader that week but he was away, on 2 days leave. We do not know who was Team Leader in his absence. Joan Lawrence was in the office during that week and had some recollection of the events but she was not the duty Team Leader. Neither Maria Anastasi nor Joan Lawrence could recall discussing the matter on 15

December 1992. Maria Anastasi did not feel that the matter was regarded as very urgent, since the message from the Police asked for contact the following day, and in any event a week had elapsed since the events of 9 December 1992 had been reported to Social Services. Neither she nor Carole Jennings felt it appropriate to advise the Specialist Mental Health Team, or to inform the Emergency Duty team who were to provide approved Social Worker cover on the night of 15 December 1992.

36.1.4.   In the event Maria Anastasi telephoned Inspector Gill on 16 December 1992 about his message. He said that complaints had been made by a petrified neighbour and local shopkeepers about Christopher Clunis and he asked what Social Services would do. She told him that Social services had tried to make contact but without success and that he was due to be seen on 24 December 1992. Inspector Gill seemed to be content with that information; he did not express any concern nor suggest any other action.

36.1.5.   Maria Anastasi cannot recall what she did then, but she thinks the matter would have been discussed at the end of the day. She could not recall discussing the matter with Joan Lawrence or anyone else. Joan Lawrence recalls talking to Maria Anastasi about the matter but could not tell us what time of day the discussion took place. It appears to have been decided to contact Dr Seargeant at Friern Hospital and Maria Anastasi did so, but not until the morning of 17 December 1992. Joan Lawrence and Peter Townley told us that since the Police had not passed on the information for 6 days the matter may not have been seen to be of immediate urgency to them either. With hindsight, Peter Townley felt that something quicker should have been done. He felt that had full information been passed to them, an urgent Mental Health Assessment Team visit would have been organised, or a S 4 Mental Health Act 1983 assessment. With hindsight Joan Lawrence thought that the matter should have been passed to the Emergency Duty Team to follow up the matter out of hours on the night of 16 December 1992. Peter Townley agreed.

36.1.6. Inspector Gill told us that on 14 December 1992 he contacted Enfield Social Services to find out whether they had a client in Marlborough Road who had been visited on 30 November 1992. They said they had not, and suggested Haringey Social Services might help because part of Marlborough Road falls within their catchment area. He finally got through to the Wood Green Office. He left a message on 14 December 1992 asking whether they had a client at 112 Marlborough Road who had been visited on 30 November 1992. He told us that they replied on Tuesday 15 December 1992 to the effect that they did have a client at 112 Marlborough Road but they had not been able to see him and therefore could not give him a description. As far as he was concerned that was the end of his involvement with the matter. He denied ever knowing the name of Clunis until June 1993. He denied giving the name Clunis to the Social Workers at Haringey. He denied that they had given the name to him.

36.2. COMMENT

36.2.1. We have considered Inspector Gill's evidence with care. It is clear that by 14 December 1992 a link had been made between the man who was visited at 112 Marlborough Road on 30 November 1992 by police officers with a Mental Health Assessment Team, and the person who had been waving a screwdriver in the streets on 9 December 1992. Once Inspector Gill had got through to Haringey and they agreed they

had a client at 112 Marlborough Road we are of the view that when he was trying to iden-
tify that person he would have been bound to have asked for his name. Simply to ask for a
description and not to ask for the name strikes us as incredible.

36.2.2. We find that Inspector Gill telephoned Haringey Social Services on 15 December
1992. We accept Carole Jennings' statement that she was given the name " Clunis" by
Inspector Gill when she rang him back in response to his message on 15 December 1992.
She wrote down the name and the message and handed it to Maria Anastasi who made a
contemporaneous note in Christopher Clunis' file. Maria Anastasi clearly knew the name
when she telephoned Inspector Gill on 16 December 1992. Inspector Gill has no recollec-
tion of either of these two telephone calls. We find that they occurred. Inspector Gill said
he did not want to visit 112 Marlborough Road because he did not know the identity of the
person he was looking for. It was put to him that Mrs Parashar could have given a
description as could her son and his friends. Inspector Gill said that none of them really
had reported the matter formally. We are very reluctant to say it but we do not accept
Inspector Gill's evidence.

36.2.3. It seems that the police had made the connection between the man at 112
Marlborough Road who was visited by the Mental Health Assessment Team on 30
November 1992 and the man who perpetrated a series of assaults on 9 December 1992.
The first person to make the connection was PC Sullivan, as did Inspector Delahay who
informed Inspector Gill. Inspector Gill, we find, knew Christopher Clunis' name and where
he lived. We find that he also knew that it was Christopher Clunis who had been waving a
screwdriver in the streets and talking about devils (hence the contemporaneous note by
Maria Anastasi). He should have realised that Christopher Clunis was a danger to the
public and probably to himself. A visit to 112 Marlborough Road with or even without a
Mental Health doctor and approved social worker would have resolved any mysteries
which still remained. He did not inform Haringey Social Services until 15 December 1992
and he did nothing to ensure that Christopher Clunis was safe. It is our view that the
police were thereby not properly protecting the public from potential harm.

37.0. FRIERN HOSPITAL CONTACT WITH THE HOUSING EMERGENCY GROUP

37.1. 15 DECEMBER 1992

37.1.1. On 15 December 1992 Dr Seargeant telephoned the Housing Emergency group and spoke to Kieran Gillan. He made a full note of that telephone call. She said she was concerned that Christopher Clunis had been discharged form Guy's Hospital so quickly. She told him that Christopher Clunis had a history of disturbed and violent behaviour including an allegation of stabbing which was only dropped because the victim disappeared. She said the incident had occurred in a homeless persons' hostel and that Christopher Clunis had only been prescribed oral medication. She pointed out that he had missed an appointment but had called in "to her department" when he had behaved perfectly normally. This can only refer to his visit to Social Services on 1 December 1992. She asked to be kept informed and gave her telephone and bleep numbers.

37.1.2. Dr Seargeant told us she recalled making a telephone call and speaking to Kieran Gillan. She had thought she had made the telephone call earlier than 15

December 1992 but she made no note and we are satisfied from the evidence we have heard from Kieran Gillan and his contemporaneous records that the telephone call was made on 15 December 1992. Dr Seargeant could not think of any reason why she was prompted to make such a telephone call on that date.

37.1.3. Kieran Gillan wrote the record on the same day as the telephone call and has no reason to doubt the accuracy of the recorded date. He told us he was worried by this telephone call and passed on the message to a colleague who had particular charge of single persons' accommodation. The colleague contacted Parkland Road Hostel which is a residential hostel for those suffering from mental illness and the completed application was taken round by hand to the Hostel on 17 December 1992. Kieran Gillan told us that Parklands Road would deal with the matter in one or two days, by visiting the client, assessing him and then coming to a decision whether to offer him a place. Because they saw the matter as one of urgency, they did not wait to obtain Christopher Clunis' consent to the application to reside at Parklands Road Hostel. Furthermore it was thought that the Parklands Road assessment team would be able to assess Christopher Clunis very much better, with their professional expertise in psychiatric illness, than could a case worker from the Housing Emergency Group.

38.0 HARINGEY SOCIAL SERVICES CONTACT WITH FRIERN HOSPITAL

38.1. THURSDAY 17 DECEMBER 1992

38.1.1. On 17 December 1992 at 11.30 am Maria Anastasi telephoned Dr Seargeant but she was doing a Ward round. She asked her to return the call. Dr Seargeant rang back at lunchtime and spoke to the duty worker, who was in fact Chris Diakou. She was told of the Police message that Christopher Clunis had been acting in an aggressive manner and threatening people with a screwdriver. Dr Seargeant advised that a Mental Health Assessment Team would have to be organised as soon a possible but according to Chris Diakou's note she wished to check which Hospital should be dealing with the case, Friern or Chase Farm. The duty worker telephoned Miss Ursula Robson, who was the duty Approved Social Worker for that day. We have heard evidence from Ursula Robson. We were impressed by Ursula Robson and the way she endeavoured to try and rectify the situation that had by then arisen.

38.1.2. Ursula Robson has worked in the Children and Family Team at Wood Green since 1975. She has been an Approved Social Worker for a number of years. She told us that if a case comes to her as Approved Social Worker and it has some difficulty or complexity then she would carry on dealing with it, even though her duty rota had ended, until she had dealt with the particular problem. She recognised that not all Approved Social Workers did that.

38.1.3. Dr Seargeant telephoned Ursula Robson at about 1.30pm and queried whether Christopher Clunis was covered by Enfield or Haringey Social Services. Ursula Robson was rather surprised about that since she felt the matter should have been resolved long before 17 December 1992, but she subsequently checked that he was indeed Haringey's responsibility. Dr Seargeant said she would check to see if Chase Farm or Friern Hospital was responsible for providing hospital care. Dr

Seargeant recalled that Ursula Robson was going to make some further enquiries before a Mental Health Assessment Visit was organised. Dr Seargeant told us she could not have been available that afternoon to do a visit. Ursula Robson then rang the Housing Emergency Group who after a long search were able to tell her that Christopher Clunis was placed at Maidstone Hotel but that he was soon to be moved to Parkland Road Hostel in Haringey.

38.1.4. She telephoned the Maidstone Hotel at 2.30pm and left a message for someone to ring her back. A person from the Head Office of the Maidstone Property Group telephoned Miss Robson at about 4 pm and said they had no concerns about Christopher Clunis; he had been very quiet and they had no complaints about him. They did not know of any complaints to the Police.

38.1.5. In the meantime Ursula Robson had read the file; she told us that Julian Green's notes in respect of the S.3 Mental health Act detention Order were in the file as were the Guy's S.117 aftercare forms. She felt considerable anxiety about the file because there was evidence of Christopher Clunis having a history of violence and yet nothing had been done as a matter of urgency. She was surprised that no visit had been arranged before 24 December 1992. She was surprised that the case had not been transferred to the specialist Mental Health Team.

38.1.6. At 4.30pm Dr Seargeant telephoned Ursula Robson again to say that Chase Farm would be taking responsibility. Ursula Robson said that she would carry on with the matter since Christopher Clunis was soon to be transferred to Parklands Road Hostel in Haringey. Dr Seargeant then said that if that were the case, Friern would continue with his care. Ursula Robnson said she would call at his address later that day and then set up an Assessment for the following day, Friday 18 December 1992. She told Dr Seargeant the further information she had discovered. Dr Seargeant said that although she was worried, she was less concerned when she heard that the incident with the screwdriver had occurred some days previously and that he had been fine in the meantime. She agreed with the Assessment taking place the following day. Dr Seargeant told us that she felt a full assessment had to be made, not just a domiciliary visit, because no one had seen him save for the Approved Social Worker.

38.1.7. Ursula Robson told us that she did indeed call, unaccompanied, at 112 Marlborough Road, but there was no reply. She later wrote a letter to Christopher Clunis at 7 pm which she delivered to his address that evening, asking him to call in the next day at 11 am. On 18 December 1992 Ursula Robson waited for Christopher Clunis to come in and told the Team Leader of the Advice and Assessment team, Peter Townley, that in her view the case should be transferred to the Mental Health Team. It was Peter Townley who told her, later that morning, that Christopher Clunis had been arrested for murder.

38.2. COMMENT

38.2.1. *In our view Haringey Social Services did not respond quickly enough to Inspector Gill's telephone call on 15 December 1992, because of lack of supervision and management of the Advice and Assessment Team. We felt that Ursula Robson tried very hard to cope with the situation in which she found herself and that in the space of a few hours, she did more to find out about Christopher Clunis than others had done over the previous 2 months. She did draw the threads together and was trying to mobilise action. She was delayed by the continuing uncertainty from Dr Seargeant as to which psychiatric service would be responsible for Christopher Clunis, but nevertheless took action. By the time of her potentially dangerous visit alone to Christopher Clunis' home address, he had already killed Jonathan Zito.*

39.0. THE DEATH OF JONATHAN ZITO – 17 DECEMBER 1992

39.0.1. We have received much of the evidence obtained by the Police in the prosecution of Christopher Clunis. Detective Inspector Webster was extremely helpful in collecting the information together and summarising it for us. He was able to confirm to us that there was no video recording of the events at Finsbury Park Tube Station but he sent us a tape recording and a summary of the words spoken by the train driver and London Transport central communications point. We are indebted to him and repeat here much of what he described in his report.

39.0.2. Mr Jonathan Zito was born on the 8 February 1965 in Italy but spent most of his life in the United States of America. He then returned to Italy where he lived and worked until he met his wife, Mrs Jayne Zito. They were married in September 1992 in Italy and set up their matrimonial home in North London. Jonathan Zito obtained employment in London as a catering manager as a short term measure, but was by profession a musician and was described by his family as a talented musician, composer and artist. He had an unassuming manner, a gentle and sensitive nature and was liked by all who knew him.

39.1. 17 DECEMBER 1992 – THE JOURNEY TO GATWICK AIRPORT

39.1.1. On Thursday 17 December 1992 at about 11.40 am, Jonathan Zito went to Watford Junction railway station and met a friend who had previously offered to take him to Gatwick Airport to meet his family. They were flying into the UK to spend the Christmas holidays with Jonathan and Jayne Zito.

39.1.2. After some delay at the airport, Jonathan Zito's family arrived and after greeting them and introducing his friend, it was decided that the friend would take the majority of the Zito family back home in his car. Due to lack of space in the car, Jonathan and his brother Mr Christopher Zito would travel back together on public transport. The majority of the family were then driven to Jonathan's home address and, on arrival, they were surprised that he and his brother had not yet arrived.

39.2. THE JOURNEY HOME

39.2.1. Jonathan Zito and his brother had in the meantime caught a British Rail train from Gatwick Airport to Victoria station, London. At Victoria they changed trains and caught a northbound Victoria line Underground train to Finsbury Park Station. At Finsbury Park they had intended to change trains once more, and to catch a northbound Piccadilly line train to Turnpike Lane station from where they would walk the short distance home.

39.3. FINSBURY PARK TUBE STATION

39.3.1. The two brothers reached the northbound Piccadilly line Underground platform at approximately 3.45 pm. They stood near the edge, towards the south end of the platform, a few feet from the connecting archway with the Victoria line platform. As they waited for a train they began to chat to one another. At this time there were other people also on the platform waiting for a train. Estimates given by various witnesses put the numbers at anything up to 75, scattered along the length of the platform.

39.3.2. Also on the platform, in the vicinity of the connecting archway, was Christopher Clunis. He was seen by a number of independent witnesses to be shabbily dressed and acting in a strange manner, and having such a unusual appearance that it drew their attention to him. One described him as a man "strolling around within a small radius" and of a strange and generally shabby appearance another stated he was "moving his arms and legs whilst remaining stationary, almost like a dance" and a third became "wary" and "had a funny feeling" about him.

39.3.3. Another young witness, a schoolgirl, was also on the platform at this time, together with a schoolfriend. She describes Christopher Clunis as looking "a bit crazy" as he stared at her. She then saw him approach the Zito brothers and she believes he may have pushed one of them, as the brothers then began to move away. She then saw him take out of his right hand jeans pocket, a yellow/mustard coloured handled knife with a 4" blade. She saw Christopher Clunis open this knife halfway. She moved away.

39.3.4. The victim's brother became concerned when Christopher Clunis came up and stood right behind him. Additional independent witnesses who had not initially taken any notice of Christopher Clunis also saw him standing close behind the brothers. He stood so close behind Christopher Zito near the edge of the platform that he became concerned for his safety and stepped sideways and away from the edge. He then motioned discreetly to his brother to move away also and join him. At this point nothing had been said between Christopher Clunis and the brothers. Indeed it is thought that Jonathan Zito had no idea that Christopher Clunis was causing any concern or that he was close behind him.

39.3.5. Christopher Clunis then swung out with his right hand extended in a circular motion, hard and fast, from behind and around Jonathan Zito's right shoulder, holding a knife in his clenched fist. He struck him fiercely in the face with a knife. People on the platform all watched in horror as Christopher Clunis attacked the victim. The 'thud' made by the blow attracted the attention of another witness. He looked and saw Christopher Clunis pull the knife from Jonathan Zito's head and heard him say calmly to Christopher Zito: "Come on then".

39.3.6. Jonathan Zito staggered forward into his brother's arms who began to try and walk him backwards, away from the attacker. He was bleeding heavily and eventually fell slowly onto the platform as a train was arriving. All the witnesses only described one blow to the victim's head. Later postmortem examination revealed however that he had suffered three facial injuries.

39.3.7. The Piccadilly line northbound train that was arriving at the platform at the time of the attack consisted of six carriages. As the train emerged from the tunnel, the driver noticed on the platform someone falling to the ground who appeared to be seriously injured, bleeding from his head or neck. Concerned that he might fall onto the track, the driver applied maximum brakes and then saw another person take hold of this person as he fell. When he brought the train to a halt at the end of the platform, he opened the doors and raised the alarm via the Piccadilly line controller, over the train radio. He then looked out onto the platform and saw many people getting on and off the train. He could not see the scene of the incident through the crowd.

39.3.8. At this point, Christopher Clunis without any sign of remorse or concern calmly walked away, and when the train had stopped and the doors had opened, he was seen to board the last carriage and sit down. A witness alerted the driver to the fact that Christopher Clunis had got onto the train and he was then advised by his controller to close the doors and hold the train on the platform, which he did.

39.3.9. Someone went to a platform telephone to call for an ambulance and also pressed two platform alarm buttons to summon help. He then went to the end carriage where he saw Christopher Clunis sitting between other passengers as if nothing had happened. A number of members of the public had gathered at the scene, tended the victim and attempted to render first aid. The ambulance and police arrived. An emergency 'blue call' was made over the ambulance radio to alert the Hospital and the ambulance left Finsbury Park Station, bound for the Whittington Hospital, where an emergency medical team was standing by.

39.3.10. A witness took police officers to the last carriage of the train where she positively identified Christopher Clunis as the man responsible for the assault. The doors to the carriage at this time were still closed and he was sitting down between passengers. That end of the platform was then cleared of members of the public and the doors to the last carriage were opened. The passengers on this carriage were asked to leave by police, which they did, with the exception of Christopher Clunis who was told to remain seated.

39.3.11. He was told to stand up which he did. He was then told that he was being arrested for an assault; cautioned at 4.05 pm to which he made no reply. He was then placed in handcuffs. He was searched and in his left hand trouser pocket, an officer found a bloodstained wooden handled folding knife.

39.4. THE WHITTINGTON HOSPITAL

39.4.1. At the Whittington Hospital the London ambulance was met by a hospital emergency medical team. Attempts were made to resuscitate Jonathan Zito as by this time he had no heart, pulse or spontaneous breathing. However, despite the efforts made by the medical team, he died.

39.4.2. Later that evening at the St Pancras Public Mortuary, Camden, London N1, a postmortem examination was carried out. Three stab wounds were found to the victim's head. One had penetrated on a slightly upwards track over the eye and into the brain, causing haemorrhage. The Pathologist was of the opinion that a wound had penetrated the brain and he gave the cause of death as "a stab wound to the head".

39.5. HOLLOWAY POLICE STATION

39.5.1. At Holloway Police Station it was noticed that Christopher Clunis appeared 'slow' and possibly educationally subnormal. He had initially told the custody officer that he was of no fixed abode but on correspondence found in his possession it was discovered he had an address at 112 Marlborough Road, London, N22. The Forensic Medical Examiner was called concerning his fitness to be detained, and the Duty Solicitor was called.

39.5.2. The doctor described Christopher Clunis as having generally an aggressive manner and giving the impression he was suffering from a psychotic personality disorder. He was however found fit to be detained. Due to the likelihood of Christopher Clunis suffering some sort of mental deficiency or illness and the fact that enquiries made concerning relatives at his home address had proved negative, the assistance of a social worker trained in mental health matters was sought to act as the appropriate adult.

39.5.2. Christopher Clunis was then informed that he was being arrested for an offence of murder; cautioned at 8.45 pm and asked: "Do you understand?" to which he replied: "Yes." It was also arranged that he should be observed constantly by a uniformed police officer outside his cell for his own welfare. This was continued throughout his detention at the police station. Mr Martin Taube, Solicitor, arrived that night at the police station to relieve the previous solicitor.

39.5.3. In the meantime the officers conducting a search of Christopher Clunis' home address discovered that he occupied a bedsitting-type room in the house, which was divided into a number of flats. His room was on the ground floor at the front of the premises and found to be in a filthy condition. An Officer recovered some medication and a quantity of correspondence.

39.5.4. Throughout the morning and into the early afternoon, numerous enquiries were made to obtain the attendance of a psychiatrist to examine Christopher Clunis. Dr Seargeant was telephoned by the Police on the morning of 18 December 1992 asking her to assess Christopher Clunis who was in custody. She suggested that someone from Guy's Hospital might be more useful since they had knowledge of him, but in the event no one from Guy's was willing to attend. She discussed the matter with Dr Taylor who agreed to go to the Police Station to assess him. At 2.05 pm, Dr Sarah Taylor, Consultant Psychiatrist from Friern Hospital arrived at the police station, and in the presence of Martin Taube examined Christopher Clunis in his cell. As the result of Dr Taylor's examination she informed the custody officer that Christopher Clunis was not fit for interview. She stated she could not be sure he understood; he had difficulty in thinking clearly; and any answers given in interview would be completely unreliable.

39.5.5. At 3.45 pm, Christopher Clunis was taken into the custody office, where he was formally charged with the murder of Jonathan Zito on the 17 December 1992, at Finsbury Park Underground station. When further cautioned at 3.46 pm, he made no reply.

39.5.6. DI Webster described this tragic case as "an unprovoked and savage attack by Christopher Clunis armed with a knife on a young man going about his lawful business waiting for a train on the platform, together with his brother."

39.6. HMP PENTONVILLE

39.6.1. Dr Kennedy, Consultant Forensic Psychiatrist from Friern Hospital was asked to assess Christopher Clunis on 22 December 1992 when he was on remand in HMP Pentonville. He found him to be probably psychotic and recommended urgent transfer to hospital under S. 48 Mental Health Act 1983. Christopher Clunis was transferred to Rampton Hospital.

40.0. CHRISTOPHER CLUNIS' TRIAL 28 JUNE 1993

40.0.1. Christopher Clunis pleaded not guilty to murder but guilty to manslaughter at the Old Bailey on 28 June 1993. That was accepted by the prosecution in the light of his previous and continuing serious psychiatric condition and the trial Judge, Mr Justice Blofeld, accepted that it was a proper plea.

40.0.2. Mr Justice Blofeld accepted the evidence of Dr Shubsachs, Consultant Forensic psychiatrist at the Rampton Hospital, that Christopher Clunis was a grave and immediate danger to the public; and the evidence of Dr Burke, Consultant Forensic Psychiatrist at St George's Hospital, that Christopher Clunis' dangerousness should not be under-estimated. Before he sentenced Christopher Clunis the Judge said this, "...I have come to the conclusion that it is in the public interest for you to go to Rampton Hospital. ...there must be no question whatever of your being released while there is the remotest chance of your being any danger to your fellow human beings." He made an Order under S 37 Mental Health Act 1983 with a restriction Order under S 41.

41.0. RAMPTON HOSPITAL

41.0.1. Christopher Clunis has remained at Rampton Hospital since 28 June 1993. We went to see him there on 21 September 1993.

41.0.2. We found him to be an intellingent and apparently easy going man, articulate and with a good sense of humour. We asked him to tell us what he could recall of his experiences and treatment over the years since he had first become ill. He recognised that, beginning with the period when he returned from Jamaica, he was not the same man that he had been before. He recalls being muddled, hallucinated and finding that he could not look after himself. His subsequent memory of admissions to hospitals or hostels and of the care he received, is of needing help, but not knowing how to ask for it; of lack of explanation as to what he was suffering from; of frustration that he was not being involved in the decisions that were being made for him; and an absence of planned help towards settling down in a home of his own.

41.0.3. He thought that some of the people who had sought to help him had tried very hard, but seemed not to understand his needs. He wanted to return to North London but said he had no choice in the matter. "A person in my position has not got the availability of choice." He told us that at some stage he returned to the pleasures of his early years, for example, just looking at the books in Wood Green Library was "damn near heaven." He also described frustrations when he wanted to alter his medication because of unpleasant side effects.

41.0.4. He was not willing to talk to us about the stabbing of Jonathan Zito.

41.0.5. Since Christopher Clunis' arrival at Rampton Hospital, Dr Alexander Shubsachs, Consultant Forensic Psychiatrist, has been his Responsible Medical Officer. We heard evidence from Dr Shubsachs. He told us that Christopher Clunis has made slow and steady progress and that he has become clearer in his mind, and less irritable and suspicious. He is now more friendly and outgoing but will still evade discussion of issues which he does not want to discuss. He continues to show evidence of a lifelong illness, which in Dr Shubsach's view will be difficult to treat completely.

41.0.6. As the Doctor who has worked with him most closely and at the greatest length, Dr Shubsachs told us that he saw Christopher Clunis as a man who has been "quite easily half treated" by control of his more florid symptoms. He observed that Christopher Clunis can appear superficially very well and that it is only by spending some time exploring his thinking that it is possible to detect underlying delusional ideas. He said that decisions about Christopher Clunis' future management will be approached very cautiously.

41.1. COMMENT

41.1.1. *We could understand how it was very possible to think that Christopher Clunis was well, if discussion with him was superficial and short lived. We found in our interview with him that it was only after some time that he began to demonstrate bizarre ideas and thoughts. We recognise that the inexperienced doctor or social worker might well have found it difficult to assess him when he was not in a psychotic state. From all we have heard during our Inquiry we agree with Dr Shubsachs that Christopher Clunis remains a danger to the public.*

SECTION IV

42.0. DEFICIENCIES IN THE CARE GIVEN TO CHRISTOPHER CLUNIS

42.1. GENERAL OBSERVATIONS

42.1.1. As will have be clear from our comments throughout the narrative we are of the view on the evidence we have heard, that Christopher Clunis' care and treatment was a catalogue of failure and missed opportunity. We do not single out just one person, service or agency for particular blame. In our view the problem was cumulative; it was one failure or missed opportunity on top of another. As a result of these numerous failures and omissions by a number of people and agencies, in our view Christopher Clunis was not provided with the good and effective care that he should have received from the time that he first attended hospital in London in July 1987 until the time he stabbed Jonathan Zito in December 1992. We consider that a lack of resources also played a part in that failure and missed opportunity. While we have found that some individuals, some services and some agencies carried out their respective roles well and to Christopher Clunis' advantage, we feel that such care was all too rare. Hence he received care and treatment that was not effective in keeping him well or the public safe.

42.1.2. We are very concerned that these failures may well be reproduced all over the country, in particular in poor inner city areas. We have heard time and again throughout the Inquiry, that Christopher Clunis is not alone, that there are many more like him living in the community who are a risk either to themselves or others.

42.1.3. We have identified and set out in the course of the narrative in Section III, many deficiencies in the care given to Christopher Clunis, since he began to suffer from paranoid schizophrenia. We do not intend to repeat all of those matters here. We now wish to concentrate on those matters of general concern that affect the provision of care in the community.

42.2. MATTERS OF PARTICULAR CONCERN

42.2.1. THERE WERE IMPORTANT FAILURES IN THE FOLLOWING RESPECTS:

1. to communicate, pass information and liaise between all those who were or should have been concerned with Christopher Clunis' care in the widest sense of that word; Consultant Psychiatrists and members of the Consultant Team; Nursing Staff; General Practitioners; Community Psychiatric Nurses; Social Workers; the Police; the Crown Prosecution Service; the Probation Service; hostel staff; people who provided care from the private sector; and

Christopher Clunis' family. Without proper communication and liaison, there cannot be effective care either in hospital or in the community.

2. to contact and involve the pateint's family and General Practitioner in the provision of care.

3. to obtain an accurate history, or to verify it.

4. to consider or assess Christopher Clunis' past history of violence and to assess his propensity for violence in the future.

5. to plan, provide or monitor S 117 Mental Health Act 1983 aftercare.

6. to manage or oversee provision of health and social services for the patient/client.

7. to provide assertive care when the patient is living in the community and to note and act upon warning signs and symptoms to prevent a relapse.

8. to identify the particular needs of homeless itinerant mentally ill patients on discharge from hospital, to keep track of such persons and to provide for their care even when they cross geographical boundaries.

9. to provide qualified social workers, including sufficient numbers of Approved Social Workers, to assess all new referrals and to provide supervision and leadership.

10. of the Police adquately to recognise and deal appropriately with mentally ill people.

11. to conduct an internal inquiry that was fair, objective and independent.

42.2.2. THERE WAS A SHORTAGE OF THE FOLLOWING IMPORTANT RESOURCES:

12. of beds in Regional Medium Secure Units for the population in the London Inner City area.

13. of beds in general psychiatric wards for the population in the London Inner City area.

14. of a range of health service accommodation for those patients who require rhabilitation or for those patients who cannot cope in the community on their own.

15. of a range of accommodation, providing varying degrees of care and supervision for patients on discharge from hospital or for patients who would otherwise relapse and then require hospital admission.

16. of sufficient numbers of Doctors who are approved under S 12 Mental Health Act 1983.

17. of sufficient numbers of social workers trained and experienced in mental illness.

42.2.3. THE FOLLOWING TENDENCIES WERE NOTED REPEATEDLY:

18. to overlook or minimise violent incidents.

19. to care and treat the acute episode of illness without also providing long term care.

20. to allow geographical boundaries to interfere with or curtail proper provision of care.

21. to postpone decisions or action when difficulty was encountered or perhaps because the patient was threatening, and intimidating, and possibly because he was big and black.

SECTION V

RECOMMENDATIONS

43.0. GENERAL OBSERVATIONS

43.0.1. We feel that it is important to emphasise, as many witnesses have reminded us, that the vast majority of mentally ill patients are living safely in the community. Furthermore the vast majority of those who suffer from schizophrenia are also living safely in the community. But there are other patients who are not receiving the care and treatment that they require to ensure that they are safe, and that the public are protected.

43.0.2. We have identified during the course of the narrative in Section IV several deficiencies in the care of Christopher Clunis. It will be self evident how some of those deficiencies may be rectified for the future. We do not intend to set out the obvious but to concentrate on those areas where we feel that we can usefully suggest recommendations for the better provsion of care in the community.

43.0.3. We make recommendations in the hope that by following them, patients will be able to live safely in the community. We do not delude ourselves that we can provide every answer. What we seek to do is to try and ensure that the terrible tragedy that has befallen Jonathan Zito and Christopher Clunis does not occur again.

44.0. THE PRINCIPLES UNDERLYING S 117 MENTAL HEALTH ACT 1983 AFTERCARE AND THE CARE PROGRAMME APPROACH

44.0.1. S 117 Mental Health Act 1983 and the Care Programme Approach under Health Circular (90)23/LASS letter 90/11 require Health Services and Social Services to provide, in co-operation with voluntary agencies, aftercare services for patients on their discharge from hospital. S 117 comes into play when the patient has been detained under the Act in hospital. The Care Programme Approach comes into play for other mentally ill patient on discharge from hospital.

44.0.2. We are concerned that doctors, nurses and social workers who are primarily responsible for providing this aftercare may not fully understand that the principles underlying S 117 and Care Programme Approach aftercare are the same. We therefore set out the common principles as we understand them. Although a great deal of very helpful guidance has been published by the Department of Health and others as to the way the Care Programme Approach should work, we are driven to say that we found that the terms in which such advice has been given, was often difficult to understand and couched in unhelpful jargon. We are sure that it is in everyone's interests; that is in the interests of the patient, those who care for the patient, the patient's relatives and the general public, that official guidance should try to be clear and simple. We suggest the following recommendations as a guide to aftercare.

44.0.3. RECOMMENDATIONS

(i) The aftercare needs of each individual patient must be assessed by health and social services before the patient is discharged into the community. Such assessment must take into account the patient's own wishes and choices.

(ii) A plan of care must be formulated for each individual patient, under the direction of the Consultant Psychiatrist under whose care the patient has been admitted.

(iii) The plan must be formulated by all those who will afterwards be responsible for providing any part of the aftercare, so that the plan is made by a team of people who work in a variety of different fields. Such a team for convenience is called the multi-disciplinary team. The aftercare plan must be recorded in detail and a copy of the plan must be given to the patient and to all those who are to provide care.

(iv) The plan of care must fully consider and provide for both the immediate and long term needs of the patient.

(v) The Consultant Psychiatrist with responsibility for the patient must assess, together with the multi-disciplinary team, the risk of the patient harming himself or others.

(vi) Members of the multi-disciplinary team should be aware that aftercare is not provided by medication alone, although it is obviously a useful part of the armoury. There is always a need to help the patient come to terms with his illness and for the patient to have proper contact with those people who will be providing him with aftercare.

(vii) A keyworker must be agreed who will act to coordinate the care that has been planned by the multi-disciplinary team.

(viii) All members of the team should be alerted to signs and symptoms in the patient which may indicate that the patient is likely to relapse. Such signs and symptoms may be identified by the doctors but may also be identified by the patient himself or his relatives or friends. Non compliance with medication should be recognised as a significant pointer to a relapse.

(ix) The aftercare which is provided must be properly coordinated and supervised; it is severely to the patient's detriment if each member of the team acts in isolation. The Consultant Psychiatrist and Care Manager from social services must together be responsible for supervising aftercare.

(x) It is essential that each member of the team who is providing care for the patient responds effectively to signs and symptoms which suggest that the patient is likely to relapse. Help which can be given before a crisis develops is more beneficial to the patient than the care that can be provided once the patient is in crisis.

(xi) When the patient moves from the district where he has previously been receiving care, responsibility for his after care should be formally transferred to the services responsible for his care in the district to which he moves.

(xii) Although Health and Social Services often have boundaries and catchment areas which do not overlap, proper co-operation between those who are providing

care is likely to resolve any potential problems. Catchment areas should never be allowed to interfere with proper care in the community.

(xiii) It is essential that the aftercare for patients is properly monitored by Health and Social Services.

(xiv) Any area of unmet need which is identified by the multi-disciplinary team must be brought to the attention of the managers of the Health and Social Services.

45.0. PARTICULAR CONSIDERATIONS IN ADDITION TO THE CARE PROGRAMME APPROACH FOR S 117 MENTAL HEALTH ACT 1983 AFTERCARE

45.0.1. S 117 Mental Health Act 1983 imposes a statutory obligation on Health Authorities and Social Services Authorities to provide aftercare for patients who have been detained under the Act. We consider that this is a vital provision to ensure effective care in the community. Its impact should not be diminished by any other provisions for care in the community.

45.0.2. In order to underline its significance we suggest that S 117 aftercare requires certain matters to be provided for in addition to those which follow the Care Programme Approach.

45.1 SECTION 117 FORM

45.1.1. We have seen a variety of S 117 forms which have been prepared by individual hospitals or Health Authorities. Some are good, but some are not so good. We consider that the S 117 form should be standardised to ensure uniformity of approach throughout England and Wales. Plans made at S 117 meetings and subsequent reviews should be recorded on a newly designed form, similar to other Mental Health Act 1983 documentation, the "pink forms". Information about the plan should be recorded on the form, as also should any modification of the plan, and the form should identify who in Health and Social Services is responsible for supervising the plan.

45.1.2. RECOMMENDATIONS

(i) A new form should be designed for use in all S 117 aftercare cases, similar to other forms which are presently standardised under the Mental Health Act 1983.

(ii) The form should record details of the plan that have been agreed, and should name the Consultant Psychiatrist, the Care Manager and the keyworker who together are responsible for the supervision and co-ordination of the plan.

(iii) Details of the signs and symptoms which suggest a likely relapse should be recorded as should details of the steps that the patient would like to be followed in the event of a relapse occurring. An assessment should be made as to whether the patient's propensity for violence presents any risk to his own health or safety or to the protection of the public.

(iv) Decisions and further plans that are made subsequently at S 117 review meetings, should be recorded on the form as should the decision to discharge the patient from S 117 aftercare.

45.2. SECTION 117 REGISTER

45.2.1. We consider that the S 117 plan should be lodged with the Mental Health Act Commission, just as other lists are maintained pursuant to the Mental Health Act 1983 and Regulations made thereunder, but always subject to strict confidentiality. When the patient presents in a new district a doctor or social worker will have immediate access to the S 117 Register to find out if the patient is already subject to a S 117 aftercare plan.

45.2.2. The Register should contain the following information only: the patient's name (and any known aliases), the patient's date of birth, a description of the patient, the name of the patient's General Practitioner, the name of the patient's Responsible Medical Officer and the name of the last hospital at which the patient was detained, together with telephone and Facsimile numbers of the relevant hospital. Such information would enable ready identification of the patient who is subject to s 117 aftercarecare and would indicate whence information about the patient could be obtained.

45.2.3. RECOMMENDATION

(v) A nationally based Register for patients subject to S 117 Mental Health Act 1983 aftercare should be set up, where information which leads to ready identification of the patient would be stored, and which would indicate whence confidential information about the patient could be obtained.

45.3. KEYWORKERS

45.3.1. We consider that the role of a keyworker in the provision of S 117 aftercare should be undertaken by qualified and experienced Social Workers or Community Psychiatric Nurses. The keyworker should have direct access to the patient's Responsible Medical Officer. The patient and his family, and members of the multidisciplinary team must have ready access to the keyworker. In our view the role of the keyworker is crucial to the co-ordination and supervision of aftercare, although ultimate responsibility must remain with the Responsible Medical Officer and Care Manager.

45.3.2. RECOMMENDATION

(vi) The nominated keyworker in S 117 aftercare should always be a qualified and experienced Social Worker or Community Psychiatric Nurse.

45.4. BEFRIENDER/ADVOCATE

45.4.1. We are concerned that the patient very often considers that the S 117 Mental Health Act 1983 aftercare plan is made at his expense rather than for his benefit. Although it is vital that the patient should, himself, participate in the formation of the plan, we consider that the patient needs someone to be his ally/befriender/advocate in relation to S 117 aftercare. That befriender should attend all S 117 meetings with the patient, should champion his cause, and should ensure that action which is supposed to happen under the plan, does in fact happen. If there is a failure to provide a service that has been agreed or if the befriender becomes aware of an area of need which has not been catered for, he should have access to the keyworker to prompt action. The befriender would be assertive in keeping in touch with the patient and in picking up any signs or symptoms of relapse, just as a caring relative would do. The befriender would only be able to relinquish responsibility when another befriender has agreed to take on the role.

45.4.2. We envisage the befriender as being a relative or friend of the patient or a volunteer. Volunteers would be able to join a local panel of befrienders after they have received training in basic mental health skills. The patient would have to agree to a particular volunteer being his befriender.

45.4.3. RECOMMENDATIONS

(vi) Every patient, subject to S. 117 Mental Health Act 1983 aftercare, should have a nominated relative, friend or volunteer to act as his befriender/advocate, unless the patient expressly states to the contrary.

(vii) Statutory Authorities and Voluntary Agencies working in the field of mental health should recruit, train and support members of the public who wish to be S 117 befrienders.

(viii) A copy of the current aftercare plan should be given to the befriender.

45.5. S 117 PLANNING ACROSS BOUNDARIES

45.5.1. We have seen during our investigations that many problems occur in respect of the aftercare of a patient who intends to move away from the locality where he has previously been receiving aftercare. We consider that for patients subject to S 117, special provision is required to ensure proper continuation of aftercare.

45.5.2. RECOMMENDATION

(ix) Before a patient, who is subject to S 117 aftercare, moves from the area where he is being cared for, a joint case conference should be held between those who are currently providing his aftercare and those who will be providing his aftercare in the future. Responsibility will remain with the original multi-disciplinary team unless and until S 117 aftercare is effectively transferred and a new S 117 form is completed by the new multi-disciplinary team.

45.6. MONITORING

45.6.1. In our view it is vital that Health Authorities and Social Services Departments should review S 117 forms regularly. S117 forms and the records of scrutiny and review should be presented to the Mental Health Act Commissioners on each statutory visit so that external monitoring can also be provided.

45.6.2. RECOMMENDATIONS

(x) S 117 forms should be reviewed regularly by the Hospital Managers as defined under the Mental Health Act 1983.

(xi) The Mental Health Act Commission should carry out external monitoring of S 117 forms on each statutory visit.

46.0. SUPERVISED DISCHARGE ORDERS

46.0.1. It is intended that the Supervised Discharge Order announced by the Secretary of State for Health in August 1993 will facilitate care in the community for patients who are subject to S 117 aftercare. The patient will be subject to recall to hospital if he fails to comply with the aftercare plan agreed by him and his carers.

46.0.2. By S 17(4) of the Mental Health Act 1983 the Responsible Medical Officer may recall a patient from leave of absence if he feels it is necessary to do so in the interests of the health or safety of the patient or for the protection of others. In the case of *R v Hallstrom ex p W* [1986] 2 All E R 306 the Court held that the power to detain a person in hospital for treatment could not be used as a means to attach conditions to a person as an outpatient, and that a person could not be recalled to hospital from leave of absence if he was not to be detained there for treatment. It means that leave of absence cannot be revoked, for example for failure to comply with medication, unless the patient's Responsible Medical Officer considers that the patient needs to be detained in hospital for treatment, for more than a nominal period.

46.0.3. Although the terms of S 27(5) of the Mental Health (Scotland) Act 1984 are in exactly the same terms as S 17 (4) of the Mental Health Act 1983, nevertheless the sub-section is interpreted differently in Scotland and allows patients to be recalled to hospital for the purposes of, for example, administering medication without inpatient admission.

46.0.4. In England by S 17 (5) a patient ceases to be liable to be recalled at the end of 6 months unless the patient has returned to hospital before the expiration of the 6 months of his first absence on leave, or is absent without leave at the expiration of the 6 month period. By contrast in Scotland under S 27(6) a patient only ceases to be liable to be recalled after he has ceased to be liable to be detained, and he may be detained for periods of up to 6 months from time to time.

46.0.5. We were impressed by what we have heard of the practice in Scotland under which supervision in the community is permitted by granting indefinite leave of absence to a patient but with safeguards, to ensure that supervision remains appropriate. In Scotland the patient is subject to recall without the need for detention in hospital for treatment. We were told that there is no record in Scotland of anyone who is subject to such supervision having committed murder, and that all but 15% of such patients comply readily with their treatment plan without the need for recall. All patients who are given supervised discharge in the community are visited by the Mental Welfare Commission for Scotland.

46.0.6. We consider that the Scottish practice is more beneficial to a patient's care and treatment than its English counterpart, and that the practice should be used as a model for the proposed Supervised Discharge Order. This would allow a patient to be recalled from time to time, without the necessity of having to be detained in hospital for treatment. The only further amendment we would suggest is that leave of absence should be permitted for 12 months at a time, after the initial 6 month period.

46.0.7. It is beyond our remit to specify the form of Supervised Discharge Orders but we would wish the following matters to be covered in the necessary legislation:

46.0.8. RECOMMENDATIONS

(i) A patient who is detained for treatment under the Mental Health Act 1983 may be made the subject of a Supervised Discharge Order.

(ii) The Supervised Discharge Order should contain details of a plan of care which the patient and his Responsible Medical Officer have agreed.

(iii) If the Responsible Medical Officer considers that the patient has failed to comply with the plan, or that the patient's mental health is deteriorating, the patient may be recalled to hospital.

(iv) A Supervised Discharge Order shall be capable of renewal within 6 months of the Order being made and for 12 monthly periods thereafter, but only on the same grounds as the original Order was made.

(v) Each renewal will be subject to the Mental Health Act 1983 appeal procedures.

(vi) The patient's Responsible Medical Officer, social worker and keyworker should be named in the Order as should the patient's relative or friend.

(vii) Supervised Discharge Orders should be lodged with and monitored by the Mental Health Act Commission.

(ix) When the patient moves to another area those who are nominated in the Order should remain responsible for his care unless and until such care is properly transferred under the Order.

47.0. SPECIAL SUPERVISION GROUP OF PATIENTS WHO NEED SPECIAL CARE

47.0.1. We emphasise again that the vast majority of those people who suffer from schizophrenia live safely in the community. However as indicated at the beginning of our Report we have been very troubled by the fact that during the period of our investigations there have been repeated reports of serious and violent acts committed by a very small number of patients who suffer from severe mental illness. Christopher Clunis is one of such patients. In our view, the serious harm that may be inflicted by severely mentally ill people on themsleves or on members of the public is a cost of care in the community which no civilised society should tolerate. There will always be some risk that harm will be inflicted. However we are concerned that such a risk should be reduced in so far as is possible.

47.0.2. In addition to those patients we have referred to in the previous paragraph, we have come to the view as our Inquiry has progressed that however good the care in the community that can be provided and however all embracing, there will always remain a small group of seriously mentally ill people who are at risk of falling through the net of care. We feel that they too need very special care and treatment involving especially close supervision and support.

47.0.3. In days gone by all such patients were confined within mental institutions so that they and the public were safe. If a similar degree of safety is to be provided when care is provided within the community then, in our view, it can only be provided by exceptional means. We consider that if the needs of that small group are not properly met, care in the community will be discredited and may be perceived as a policy which has failed. We do not think that as a society we can afford to let that happen. We are convinced, as we felt was every witness from whom we received evidence, that care in the community is the right approach for caring for the mentally ill and we have no wish to return to the days of locked, impersonal, dehumanising and undignified institutional care.

115

47.0.4. We have called that group of patients who need special supervision, the Special Supervision Group. We suggest that patients who suffer from mental disorder and who are assessed by their Consultant Psychiatrist to require close supervision and support, and who meet 2 of the following criteria, would fall into that group:

(a) patients who have been detained in hospital under the Mental Health Act 1983 on more than one occasion;

(b) patients who have a history of violence or of persistent offending;

(c) patients who have failed to respond to treatment from the general psychiatric services;

(d) patients who are homeless.

47.0.5. We consider that the Special Supervision Group needs to be cared for by a specialist multi-disciplinary team who have a limited and protected case load. The patients we are trying to identify are those who are difficult to care for, and need to be followed up intensively, with assertive and close supervision.

47.0.6. A number of witnesses, particularly Consultant Forensic Psychiatrists from whom we heard, considered that this special group would comprise appoximately 3,000 to 4,000 patients nationwide.

47.0.7. We heard evidence from Professor Tom Burns, Professor of Community Psychiatry at St George's Hospital Medical School who is currently setting up such a Specialist Team. We were impressed by his vision as well as his realistic approach. It is his view that such a group are likely to comprise the difficult to manage, or those who are not easy or attractive propositions for those who are trying to care for them. Hence he intends to limit case load to 12 patients for each worker in the Specialist Team, who will follow patients over boundaries. He told us, and this was supported by evidence from Professor Kevin Gourney, Professor of Mental health at Middlesex University, that such teams have been tried and tested in other countries, in the United States of America and in Australia, and have proved enormously successful. We were also told that although intensive care is provided by a specialist team, the work that has been done in other countries demonstrates that it is cost effective when compared with full time inpatient care.

47.0.8. At a late stage of our Inquiry we learned with interest of a project in Cambridgeshire to provide care to such a group of patients which is currently being developed by Turning Point, a Mental Health Charity.

47.0.9. From all we have heard during our Inquiry, we consider that a Special Supervision Group should be targeted for special care. It is also clear that existing mental health budgets could not provide for such Specialist Teams. The clear evidence is that such a service should be separately funded, with an arbitrator ensuring that such funds are used as intended.

47.0.10. We envisage a special role for Community Psychiatric Nurses specialising in the care of Special Supervision Group, often as key worker. They would work exclusively for the specialist team in caring for the Special Supervision Group and would have no other duties.

47.0.11. It is this Special Supervision Group whom we consider should be placed on the Supervision Register which the Secretary of State for Health has recently announced. We consider that such a Register should be held nationally, so that such patients can be readily identified as needing special care and treatment. We envisage such a Register being particularly useful in the care of the homeless or itinerant patients.

47.0.12. We consider that the Register should contain the following information only: the patient's name (and any known aliases), the patient's date of birth, a description of the patient, the name of the patient's General Practitioner, the name of the patient's Responsible Medical Officer and the name of the last hospital at which the patient was admitted, together with telephone and Facsimile numbers. Such information would enable ready identification of a patient in the Special Supervision Group as being in need of special care and treatment and would indicate from where information could be obtained about the patient. We emphasise that we do not consider that any information as to the patient's diagnosis, history, treatment or any other personal information should be kept on the register. It would simply act as a means of identifying the patient and where information about the patient is held. We consider that only those who can show a bona fide interest in knowing whether a person is registered on the list, for example, Doctors, Community Psychiatric Nurses, Social Services, the Police, and relatives of the patient should be able to learn whether the subject of their enquiry is registered on the Supervision Register and where information about that person is held. Only the patient's Consultant Psychiatrist would be empowered to decide whether information about the patient should, in fact, be passed to the person making enquiry.

47.0.13. We would hope that some patients would derive a sense of security from knowing that their names were on such a Register and would welcome the fact that as a result of being on the Register a rapid response could be made to their needs in times of crisis.

47.0.14. We understand the real concerns about confidentiality, but as a country which has embraced the policy of care in the community, we feel that a balance has to be struck between those concerns and the equally clear concerns for the safety of the patient and the safety of the public. In our view the benefits of a Register far outweigh any concerns. Such a Register would be a useful tool in identifying or tracking patients who are in the Special Supervision Group, but it is only a tool. The Register is not by itself the answer to the provision of care for patients in the Special Supervision Group; it will simply be an aid to ensuring that such patients are not lost to follow up care.

47.0.15. RECOMMENDATIONS

(i) Every psychiatric service should identify patients as part of a Special Supervision Group and should provide a Specialist Team to supervise and support the group.

(ii) New funding should be provided for that purpose.

(iii) A nationally based Supervision Register for the Special Supervision Group should be set up, where information which leads to ready identification of the

Patient would be stored, and which would indicate from where confidential information about the Patient could be obtained.

(iv) Every psychiatric service should appoint specialist Community Psychiatric Nurses to the team responsible for the Special Supervision Group whose only job is to supervise a very limited case load.

(v) Community Psychiatric Nurses should follow patients across health boundary borders until responsibility is formerly transferred to another specialist team.

48.0. CONFIDENTIALITY

48.0.1. In our view, if care in the community is to be provided properly by a multi-disciplinary team, then there has to be a sharing of information about the patient between members of that team. Doctors and nurses are bound to keep information about patients confidential under their respective Codes of Practice and we understand that all professional social workers are required by their contracts of employment to maintain their client's confidentiality. We would support the idea of social workers also being bound by a professional code of conduct. It is essential that all those who may share some responsiblity for the patient's aftercare are bound by the same rule of confidentiality. With proper sharing of information the patient is more likely to receive effective aftercare.

48.0.2. We are impressed by the view that if there is a risk that the patient may harm himself or others, everyone who may provide any service to the patient, for example those who may provide housing, occupational therapy, or financial benefits, needs to know about this risk. The question of confidentiality is not an easy subject and it is beyond our remit to try and resolve the conflicting issues. But we feel that it is a vital matter which needs to be addressed and resolved urgently now that the Care Programme Approach is required for care in the community.

48.0.3. RECOMMENDATION

The Department of Health should determine, with the help of Directors of Social Services and others, how the confidentiality of mentally ill patients may be properly protected within the Care Programme Approach.

49.0. THE ASSESSMENT OF DANGEROUSNESS

49.0.1. Dr Nigel Eastman, Consultant Forensic Psyhciatrist, amongst others reminded us that, "the only decent predictor of future behaviour is past behaviour". Numerous witnesses, who are concerned to assess a patient's dangerousness, said that an accurate and verified history of the patient is vital in making such an assessment. Despite the fact that an accurate history is widely recognised to be invaluable in assessing a patient's dangerousness, we found that time and again either violent incidents were minimised or omitted from records, or referred to in the most general of terms in discharge summaries. Often histories were unavailable to those who came to care for the patient afterwards. We noted throughout our Inquiry that serious violent incidents were often only recorded in the nursing notes and not picked up by the clinicians or social workers.

49.0.2. The assessment of the risk of violence should never be a hasty guess following a simple examination of the patient's current mental state at interview. It is a skill to be learned and refreshed from time to time by anyone who has responsibility to respond to the needs of people showing disturbed behaviour. Psychiatrists and other mental health workers need to be trained in this skill as do, at the appropriate level, general practitioners and other members of the primary health care team, social workers, police and probation officers. Each may be called upon to make judgements about whether the level of risk requires action which might deprive a fellow citizen of his liberty or prevent harm to others. At the very least they should be given sufficient training to recognise the limits of their personal knowledge and to understand the role of forensic services. There are examples in the story of Christopher Clunis where poorly considered and sometimes misleading predictions led to false reassurance about his potential for dangerous behaviour.

49.0.3. We consider that it is vital for the safety of the patient and the public that accurate recording is made of any violent or potentially violent incident and that information about such an incident is included in the discharge summary. We well understand the wish not to stigmatise a patient, but in our view the safety of the patient and the public overrides such concerns. Records should be accessible to doctors who care for a patient subsequently, without the waste of time and resources that currently appears to be expended, often achieving nothing. Medical Records Departments could be charged with the collection and sending of relevant records or summaries, but only after the patient's Consultant or Registrar has agreed to the information being sent. We would like to see far more use made of Fax machines, so that clinical records and discharge summaries do not have to be photocopied and then sent, and so that originals are retained on the Medical Records Department and the chances of notes getting lost are reduced.

49.0.4. RECOMMENDATIONS

(i) An accurate record should be made of any incident of violence and the details should be included in the patient's discharge summary.

(ii) An assessment of the risk of dangerousness should be included in the discharge summary whenever the patient has acted with violence.

(iii) Everyone who has contact in his professional or service work with mentally ill people who may pose a risk of violence should have training in the assessment of dangerousness, and understand when to refer the patient for expert guidance.

50.0. SOCIAL SERVICES DEPARTMENTS

50.0.1. Although we have only looked at the practices of one Social Services Department in detail, we have received information on procedures from three others. Throughout the Inquiry we have paid special attention to the contact between social workers and the staff of other agencies, particularly at the times of Christopher Clunis' crisis and relating to the management of risks. We have found that most of the specialist social workers did possess the knowledge and skills needed to make difficult judgements, and did so appropriately.

50.0.2. It has to be said however that in Haringey Social Services Department a number of those who were untrained or lacking experience did not receive sufficient guidance or supervision from senior staff. When this coincided with a lack of understanding or sense of urgency on the part of people working in other agencies, the results were disastrous.

50.0.3. It is clear that the contribution of Approved Social Workers can be a key component in decision making and action. We have been told that the standards of their performance are felt to have improved satisfactorily over the last ten years since the introduction of national training and accreditation standards. However several witnesses have pointed out that the training of Approved Social Workers is very specific to assessment and detention of patients under the Mental Health Act 1983, which does not fully equip them to be Psychiatric Social Workers.

50.0.4. It is important that Approved Social Workers should not only perform their statutory role in the care of mentally ill people in the community. They have a special contribution at times of crisis. Their involvement with patients should be clearly set out in patients' records to facilitate on going treatment and aftercare.

50.0.5. RECOMMENDATIONS

(i) More social workers should be recruited where teams are seen to be under strength in particular if the team is involved with new referrals.

(ii) Where social services reception and referral systems are manned by unqualified or inexperienced staff, such staff must have ready access to an experienced Approved Social Worker.

(iii) Unqualified and recently qualified social workers must work under the supervision of a qualified and experienced manager and their work should be reviewed at least once every fortnight by their supervisors.

(iv) When current cases involve active danger the daily hand over and briefing arrangements for staff should ensure that the case continues to receive prompt attention.

(v) There should be close contact and liaison between social services departments and local housing agencies.

(vi) An Approved Social Worker should be available in each social services department to respond to crises and to provide advice. An Approved Social Worker should be contactable throughout the working day, as well as at night and during weekends and public holidays.

(vii) Medical recommendations leading to detention should be copied for the Approved Social Worker for his records, and a copy of the Application for Admission recommendation should be kept by him. He should also provide a report for the Hospital where the patient is to be detained and retain a copy of it for the social services file on the patient.

51.0. RESOURCES

51.0.1. It is clear from what we have been told during the Inquiry that there is a shortage of Medium Secure Unit beds within the South East Thames Regional Health

Authority. The strong impression we have received is that there is a lack of such beds in the Units which serve the whole of central London. Within the limits of our Inquiry we have not been able to discover why that should be; but we suspect that the demand for such beds is increased in an inner city area, where there is social deprivation, and where there is a substantial prison population. It may be that this increased need for Medium Secure Unit beds is reflected in every inner city area and we are concerned that the current Weighted Capitation Formula does not take these matters sufficiently into account.

51.0.2. The shortage of such beds means that some patients have to be admitted to costly private hospitals, often in an area far away from their homes. We do not consider that is in either the patient's or the public's best interests. Sometimes patients who require to be admitted to a Medium Secure Unit bed have to be contained within General Psychiatric Wards, which are not properly equipped to care for patients who are disturbed or violent. This can cause other patients on those wards to be frightened or anxious, which in turn interferes with their care and treatment. Dr Parker, Consultant Psychiatrist, told us that she regularly has patients who in her view should receive care within a Medium Secure Unit, but because of lack of beds in the Unit cannot be transferred unless and until "things go dramatically wrong".

51.0.3. We have also been told that patients who are ready to be discharged from Medium Secure Units sometimes have to be discharged into the community. We agree with a number of Forensic Pyshiatrists from whom we have heard that such discharge is inappropriate and is compounded by the fact that the patients have not received the benefit of any local rehabilitation programme. We consider that there is a need for each Medium Secure Unit to have access to local rehabilitation units, so that patients are thereafter ready to be discharged with safety, into the community.

51.0.4. During the course of our Inquiry we have learned that there are insufficient numbers of forensic psychiatrists to care for mentally ill offenders, and other mentally disordered patients, who are disturbed or violent. We recognise that Forensic Psychiatry is a relatively new speciality, but the role of the forensic psychiatrist should not, in our view, be underestimated in the care of mentally ill people who are a risk to themselves or others. However it is essential that patients are referred to the Forensic Psychiatric team for assessment and care only when necessary, so that the team is not overwhelmed. We consider that every Psychiatric Service should include one member who has a special interest in Forensic Psychiatry, to ensure that proper referrals are made.

51.0.5. We have also heard repeatedly that there are insufficient beds in general psychiatric wards in London hospitals to care for all the patients who should properly be admitted for treatment. We have heard from Dr Elizabeth Parker that Hither Green Hospital has an average bed occupancy of 120%; from Dr John Wilkins that Horton Hospital has an average of 100% - 110% bed occupancy and that the Central Middlesex Hospital has a 130% bed occupancy; and from Dr David Roy that South Western Hospital has an average of 103% -120% bed occupany. We have also learned that the average length of stay in such wards is relatively short, for example it is only 18 days at Guy's Hospital. We have been told of the great pressure on such beds, which tends to lead to premature discharge or to granting leave of absence when the Consultant considers that it would be better for the patient to stay on the ward. We have also been told that because there is a large number of homeless mentally ill people in South East London, they often fill a number of beds on General Psychiatric Wards to the exclusion of the local population, who may also need admission. Paul Ward, the Contracts Manager for Community and Priority Services for the South East London Health Authority told us, "...the threshold for getting into mental health services in inner London is starting to get higher and higher. There is an increased number of people who are not getting proper access to mental health services as a consequence, particularly informal patients."

51.0.6. We have heard from both doctors and social workers that there is a need for long or short stay 'haven type' accommodation for patients who are unable to cope in the community. There was much evidence before us that some patients just cannot live independently in the community either in the short or long term. They need a refuge or sanctuary which is medically staffed and supervised, to care for them properly. We have been told that such accommodation could also be useful to provide respite care for those who are otherwise looked after at home by their families and friends.

51.0.7. Finally we have heard from both doctors and social workers that there are insufficient residential hostels and supported housing to accommodate mentally ill patients on their discharge into the community from general psychiatric wards. Sometimes patients have to be discharged from hospital and into bed and breakfast accommodation, before they can be assessed for suitability for the hostels that are available. In our view that is not in the patient's interests and tends to encourage a relapse so that the patient once again has to be admitted to hospital, when the whole process may recur.

51.0.8. We of course realise that provision of a better range of accommodation for mentally ill people will require a considerable injection of funds for the mentally ill. However if proper care is to be provided for those unfortunate to suffer from mental illness then the only answer, in our view, is to meet the deficiencies identified to us so often by the experienced witnesses who appeared before us during the Inquiry. We have the impression that the general public would consider that money spent on keeping the mentally ill well, and the public safe, would be money well spent. The admission or on-going treatment of patients who present clear risks to themselves or the public at large should not be determined by the economics of the market place.

51.0.9. RECOMMENDATIONS

(i) An increased number of Medium Secure Unit beds within the South East Thames Regional Health Authority area is urgently needed. Furthermore urgent consideration should be given as to whether an increased number of such beds should be provided for every inner city area.

(ii) There is a clear need for the provision of rehabilitation units to be available to Regional Medium Secure Units.

(iii) An increased number of beds on general psychiatric wards in London is urgently needed. Furthermore urgent consideration should be given as to whether an increased number of such beds should be provided in every inner city area.

(iv) There is a clear need for 'haven-type' accommodation for those who cannot cope in the community.

(v) There is a clear need for a range of supervised accommodation for those who suffer from mental illness, from intensively staffed hostels with a high degree of nursing care, through warden staffed self contained units, to accommodation that is reserved for mentally ill people who can live more or less independently.

(vi) There is a clear need for an increased number of forensic psychiatrists.

(vii) Every psychiatric service should include a doctor who has a special interest in Forensic Psychiatry.

52.0. INSPECTION, MONITORING AND AUDIT

52.0.1. In the course of our inquiry, it has been noticeable how little routine attention appears to have been paid to anybody to quality or outcome measurement of the community management of mentally ill people. The same is true of the performance of staff, either as individuals or teams. There seem to have been no consequences whether the work was done well or done badly. Those who planned procedures or made policies do not appear to have checked or to know whether they were being followed. It has been difficult to understand the objectives of services other than to achieve ever more rapid turnover of inpatients. Judging from the example of Christopher Clunis from 1987 to 1992, responsibility, once a patient has left hospital, has usually been vague or misunderstood, leading staff to work in the dark. Communication has often been duplicated or not done at all.

52.0.2. In current terms, purchasers do not know what they are buying, nor do the providers know what they are selling. No one has a means of telling whether the community service provided is effective or an efficient use of resources. The old certainties and principles of care within traditional institutions which might have been too rigid have disappeared but have not been replaced.

52.0.3. There is a strong case for devising a method to formulate and spread the principles of good clinical practice in psychiatric care in the community, probably by peer review, as was formerly the role of the Health Advisory Service and still is for the Drug Advisory Service. External review needs to be supported by agreed standards of performance, which should be checked both by internal review by the service itself and by regular obligatory external visits. Some form of accreditation would give reassurance and confidence to authorities which commission services that standards have been reached by providers of the services. We have reminded ourselves that the history of the care of mentally ill people is that without external scrutiny, standards always drop, whether they are to be found within hospital or outside.

52.0.4. RECOMMENDATIONS

(i) In our view it is essential that the Department of Health sets up proper procedures for effective monitoring of psychiatric services in the community.

(ii) The Department of Health should publish the principles which community mental health services for the seriously mentally ill must follow, and declare minimum standards in manpower and facilities for all services to reach. These should be the basis of what the NHS Management Executive requires each Health Authority to commission for its community.

(iii) A duty should be imposed on service providers in their contracts with commissioning authorities to satisfy an external inspecting or accrediting body that they have currently achieved published standards of service and facilities.

(iv) The Department of Health should institute a system to inspect community mental health services every three years, and to examine the results of health and social services annual joint reviews, so that national standards may be defined, maintained and improved upon.

(v) When an internal Inquiry is carried out within a hospital or social services department it is essential that not less than 2 members of the public are included on the panel to ensure that the Inquiry is as independent and objective as possible. Such members of the public should agree not to divulge any confidenatial information learned during the Inquiry.

53.0. MENTAL ILLNESS AND OFFENDING

53.0.1. The Home Office Circular on Provision for Mentally Disordered Offenders (No 66/90) is followed by both the Police and the Crown Prosecution Service. The aim of the Circular is to ensure that a mentally disordered person who has offended against the criminal law, but only in a minor way and where the public interest does not demand prosecution, is not charged or brought to trial, but diverted to the psychiatric service for care and treatment, rather than punishment. We entirely endorse that Circular.

53.0.2. However there is little guide to interpretation within the Circular and we are concerned that sometimes, and for the most humane of reasons, an offender is not charged because he is mentally ill. In particular it seems to us that an offender who has committed a potentially serious offence, but has been prevented from causing serious harm, may be a person who is not charged at all or only charged with an offence of Breach of the Peace.

53.0.3. The Police have to make the decision whether to charge an offender who may be mentally ill. The Metropolitan Police Instruction Manual states:

"Consideration should be given to consulting the Crown Prosecution Service and informing an Approved Social Worker or Duty Psychiatrist, as appropriate, prior to charge. The Crown Prosecution Service and Approved Social Worker are to be informed of the person's condition after charge, in order that the Court may be requested to dispose of the case accordingly."

53.0.4. However, it appears from our Inquiry that sometimes the Police make the decision not to charge a mentally disordered offender without the benefit of opinion from either an Approved Social Worker or the Duty Psychiatrist. We consider that the Home Office should publish a Guide to help the Police with the interpretation of the Circular, so that, a medical opinion from the Forensic Medical Examiner is always obtained by the Police if it appears to them that an offender is suffering from mental illness, and so that the potential seriousness of the offence and the public interest is always taken into account in deciding whether to charge.

53.0.5. Once the decision is made to charge a person who is suffering from mental illness, in our view it is important that the charge properly reflects the seriousness or potential seriousness of the Offence.

53.0.6. The matter is then passed to the Crown Prosecution Service. We are told by the Crown Prosecution Service that any medical reports should be attached to the file when the papers are sent to them. We are concerned that sometimes that is not done. If a medical opinion always has to be obtained by the Police in respect of an offender who appears to them to be mentally ill, then a medical opinion which states that the offender is suffering from a mental illness, will always have to be sent to the Crown Prosecution Service with the file.

53.0.7. The Crown Prosecution Service, however, cannot and do not, take into account the Defendant's mental state or his propensity for dangerousness, in deciding whether there is sufficient evidence to prove the case against the Defendant. Only after they have decided that there is sufficient evidence to proceed to trial then they do take those matters into account, in reviewing the case and in deciding whether to proceed to trial, or to divert the offender away from the Criminal Justice System. They have told us that "the graver the offence, the less likelihood there will be that the public interest will allow of a disposal less than prosecution". In our view it is also important that the gravity, including the potential gravity, of the offence is reflected in the charge.

53.0.8. We believe that Consultant Psychiatrists and their teams are not sufficiently aware of the principles which guide the Police and Prosecution, and in our view it is imperative that they should be familiar with the Circular, and any Guide as to interpretation.

53.0.9. When a mentally disordered person charged with an offence is remanded to hospital, then in our view the Consultant Psychiatrist should consider whether it is appropriate for the patient to be detained under the Mental Health Act 1983, irrespective of the charge and the ultimate disposal of the case. Hence if a patient needs to be detained under S 3 Mental Health Act 1983 for his own health or safety, or for the protection of others, then he should be detained in hospital irrespective of the charge against him. Then if the case is dropped at any stage, or if he is found not guilty of the offence, he will not be discharged into the community unless and until those treating him consider that he is fit to be discharged from the Mental Health Act 1983 section under which he is detained.

53.0.10. While we understand that this may be a "belt and braces" recommendation, we have no doubt that it would serve the interests of the patient. He and his Nearest Relative (S11(3) Mental Health Act 1983), would know at the time the Detention Order is made that whatever happens to his case, he would have to remain in hospital until he was well enough to be discharged, that he would receive the benefit of planned discharge under S 117 Mental Health Act 1983 and that he could appeal against his detention within the existing provisions of the Mental Health Act 1983.

53.0.11. In our view this does not expose the mentally ill offender to double jeopardy; it does however ensure that he receives the care and treatment he requires.

53.0.12. It should be remembered that medical views as to a patient's proper care and treatment are not matters that a Court can take into account until after the Defendant has been convicted of the offence with which he has been charged.

53.0.13. RECOMMENDATIONS

(i) The Home Office should publish a Guide to interpretation of the Circular on Provision for Mentally Disordered Offenders (No 66/90), in which clear advice should be given as to when it is appropriate to charge someone who is mentally ill. Such advice should include guidance as to when medical opinion should be obtained, and as to what matters should be taken into consideration, including the potential seriousness of the charge and the public interest.

(ii) A medical recommendation obtained by the Police in relation to a medically disordered offender, must be sent to the Crown Prosecution Service with the papers or as soon thereafter as it is received.

(iii) The Consultant Psychiatrist who is responsible for the care of a patient, who has been charged with an offence and remanded to hospital, custody, must consider whether the patient needs to be detained for treatment under the Mental Health Act 1993, irrespective of the outcome of that charge.

54.0. THE POLICE

54.0.1. We understand from what we have been told during the Inquiry that the Police are often in the front line in the community in dealing with mentally disordered people. It is clear that such a role has substantially increased as patients have been returned to the community and long stay mental hospitals have been closed. We have the impression that some officers consider that mental health is not really police business. We are aware that the general public is often ignorant and frightened of mental illness and it may be that police officers are no exception.

54.0.2. It is our impression from the evidence we have heard, which was confirmed by two officers from the Crime and Divisional Policing Policy Branch of New Scotland Yard, that at present police officers are ill equipped to understand and deal with mentally disordered people. We have already referred within the narrative to the fact that sometimes the decision whether or not to charge an offender, who is suspected of suffering from mental illness, is made without the benefit of medical opinion.

54.0.3. Furthermore it seems that officers may not know what psychiatric services or other help is available in their locality, and they often have no idea who to contact who could provide such services.

54.0.4. In our view it is essential that police officers are properly trained to fulfil their new and increasing role in relation to mentally disordered people. They also need to learn about local services and to know who to contact. We have heard that in Hackney police officers go to meet hospital staff and patients on wards, or go out with Community Psychiaric Nurses so that they learn about mental illness and who to contact if they come across a problem. We consider that this may be just the sort of model which could be usefully followed by other Police Divisions.

54.0.5. Under S 136 Mental Health Act 1983 a police officer is empowered to remove a person to a place of safety if it appears to him that the person is suffering from mental disorder, to be in immediate need of care and control, and that it is necessary to do so in the interests of the person or for the protection of the public. Officers are clearly aware of this power and we were told that 42 of the 69 Metropolitan Police Divisions have drawn up a Code of Practice with the local health services and social services to be followed when a person is detained under S 136. We are concerned, however, that the documents used by police officers under s 136 are very varied. We consider that S 136 forms should be standardised and made a Mental Health Act "pink form". It will then be immediately recognisable by all concerned, including the patient and his family, irrespective of the place from where the patient is removed or to which the patient is transferred for treatment.

54.0.6. We have heard during our Inquiry that sometimes when the Police respond by taking a person to hospital, they find that they must remain for hours waiting for an assessment to be carried out, or find that, once an assesment has been made, the patient is simply discharged without any one informing the Police or explaining why.

54.0.7. Finally we are concerned that there seems to be so much uncertainty by the Police and others as to the form of consent necessary for disclosure of a person's medical or other records. In our view there is no magic formula or form; it is only necessary that the person whose records are sought to be disclosed, consents thereto. Generally such consent should be by way of written signed consent in order to prevent any argument thereafter, but it can be given orally. It would obviously be sensible, however, to record that fact at the time that such consent is given. The person can limit such disclosure to an individual or organisation as he wishes.

54.0.8. RECOMMENDATIONS

(i) Officers should be given proper training in mental illness. It is vital that such training should include both knowledge about mental illness and experience of those who suffer from mental illness.

(ii) S 136 Mental Health Act 1983 procedures and documentation should be standardised.

(iii) An Officer should be appointed at every Police Station to deal with mental health issues.

(iv) The Police should be encouraged to liaise with local community mental health services.

55.0. GENERAL PRACTITIONERS

55.0.1. We are concerned that General Practitioners who have responsibility for the primary care of a patient may be little involved in mental health care in the community. We are convinced that General Practitioners should play a full and active part in the Care Programme Approach for their patients. They should be invited to attend S 117 Mental Health Act 1983 aftercare conferences and should endeavour to do so. There should be far more liaison between the general psychiatric hospital staff and the patient's General Practitioner in particular in relation to his care after discharge from hospital. Detailed discharge summaries and details of the care plan should be sent promptly to the patient's General Practitioner. We consider that the use of fax machines would enable such summaries to be transmitted promptly, but until every practice has one, then we consider that summaries should reach the patient's General Practitioner within 5 working days of his discharge from hospital.

55.0.2. It should not be possible to remove a patient who is mentally ill from the General Practitioner's list, without taking steps to ensure that proper care is provided for the patient. We are impressed by the point of view that rejection by a General Practitioner suggests that the patient's care and treatment in the community has failed.

55.0.3. We consider that crisis cards or "smart cards" are a useful tool in the care of mentally ill people in the community. The card, which is a little like an organ donor card,is held by the patient and can be used in times of crisis to identify the patient and his nominated relative or friend, who will be able to pass on useful information to those caring for the patient. The evidence before us has shown however that the difficult patient will not retain such a card; it will be lost, stolen or not kept on the patient's person. While we favour crisis cards for the majority of patients who suffer from some form of mental illness, we do not consider that they are the answer for the difficult to manage patient or the patient who is severely ill. We do however think it would be sensible for General Practitioners to encourage their patients to use such a card. We suggest that the Royal College of Psychiatrists should devise an appropriate crisis card, copies of which could then be kept at General Practitioner surgeries, for patients to collect and fill in when they attend the surgery.

55.0.4. RECOMMENDATIONS

(i) General Practitioners should be informed of all aftercare plans.

(ii) General Practitioners should always be invited to attend S 117 Mental Health Act 1983 aftercare meetings, and aftercare meetings for vulnerbale or severely ill patients.

(iii) Discharge summaries should be sent to General Practitioners by Facsimile, or at the latest by post within 5 working days of discharge.

(iv) Before a General Practitioner may remove a patient from his list, whom he believes or suspects suffers from a psychiatric illness, he must obtain advice from the local Psychiatric team and follow such advice, and must inform the Family Health Services Authority of his intention to remove the patient from his list, so that the Authority can ensure that the patient is registered with a new General Practitioner as soon as possible.

(v) A General Practitioner whose patient is on the Supervision Register or the Mental Health Act 1983 Register must not remove the patient from his list without previously informing the patient's Responsible Medical Officer, and ensuring that another General Practitioner has agreed to act as the patient's General Practitioner.

(vi) The Royal College of Psychiatrists should be asked to design a crisis card for mentally ill people.

56.0. RESPONDING TO CRISES

56.0.1. We have observed during our Inquiry a lack of clear and coordinated response to a psychiatric crisis. We consider that there is a need for properly formulated plans for responding to such crises 24 hours a day. Joint plans and procedures should be formulated for each locality by Psychiatric Services and Social Services in consultation with the Police. These should be published and held by Psychiatric Services, Social Services, General Practitioners, the Police, Housing Departments and every other individual or agency that provides support for mentally disordered patients. Each patient who is considered by his Consultant Psychiatrist to be at risk of such a crisis should also be given a copy.

56.0.2. The procedures should include arrangements for each service to hand over information on current problems between its day and night workers.

56.0.3. The procedures should specify targets for response times, and should be systematically reviewed to ensure compliance and to improve upon the service for response to crisis that is provided.

56.0.4. Some of the delays in arranging the mental health assessments which we have studied were, in our opinion, unacceptably long. We were told by a number of witnesses that it is often difficult to arrange for a psychiatrist approved under Section 12 of the Mental Health Act 1983 to attend when needed. Mental Health assessments may be delayed inordinately because of the problem of assembling all the parties together.

56.0.5. RECOMMENDATIONS

(i) Each psychiatric service should actively recruit medical practitioners to make certain that there are sufficient doctors in their area who are approved under Section 12 of the Mental Health Act 1983 to ensure prompt response to requests for assessment under the Act.

(ii) We suggest that urgent requests should be met within three hours and non urgent requests within three working days. The performance of these targets must be properly monitored.

57.0. ETHNIC MINORITIES

57.0.1. We referred at the beginning of our report to our aim throughout the Inquiry to keep a close eye on any suggestion of racial prejudice. As we remarked we have not come accross any prejudice or discrimination in relation to Christopher Clunis, save in a willingness to accept too readily that he had abused drugs.

57.0.2. We have been told however, on many occasions, of the over representation of black people in those diagnosed as suffering from schizophrenia. It has also been confirmed that the proportion of black people amongst those detained under the Mental Health Act 1983 is high in relation to other ethnic groups. No one has been able to explain why that should be, but it is obviously important that young black males should not be type cast as suffering from schizophrenia unless the clinical indications warrant it. Similarly we suggest that clinicians and others who care for black mentally ill people should not be too ready to ascribe odd behaviour to the abuse of drugs.

57.0.3. Finally we would wish to enter a plea that young black people should be encouraged to become General Practitioners and Psychistrists so that the medical service is not seen to be dominated by whites or other ethnic groups.

58.0. VOLUNTEERS AND MEMBERS OF THE PUBLIC

58.0.1. We have already recommended that members of the public could act as befrienders to those who are mentally ill for the purposes of S 117 Mental Health Act 1983 aftercare. We believe that there is a vein of voluntary workers which could be tapped, who would be ready and able to help to care for mentally ill people in the community. We have heard from the Director of the Afro-Carribean Mental Health Association that black members of the public have been of considerable help in caring for black mentally ill people. We suggest that members of the public should be encouraged to offer their services, to contribute to the quality of life of those who suffer from mental illness. It appears to us that local Health and Social Services could, with the aid of the local press and media, usefully attempt to obtain the services of volunteers.

58.0.2. We also consider that many mentally disordered patients would be helped by the benefit of a 24 hour telephone line to a volunteer. Those who suffer from mental illness, perhaps even more than the rest of us, occasionally need help in the middle of the night; they need a friendly ear to advise and help them or perhaps just to put matters in perspective. We would strongly suggest that such a service be provided; we are sure that, as in all illness, prevention is better than cure, and that a friendly person at the end of a telephone may well diffuse a potential crisis.

APPENDIX 1

FACTUAL WITNESSES

WITNESSES	ORGANISATION
Alexander, Hugh	Lambeth Social Services
Anastasi, Maria	Haringey Social Services
Anderson, Dr James	Bracton Clinic
Anstead, PC Alan	Southwark Police Station
Barker, Supt. Margatet	Complaints Unit, Metropolitan Police, Edmonton
Bartlett, Nigel	Member of Public
Bee, Elizabeth	Spur House Resettlement Unit
Begum, Dr Nargis	Locum GP, Spur House Resettlement Unit
Brown, Dr Percy	HMP Belmarsh
Bryant, Michael	Lambeth Social Services
Clark, Anthony	Bexley Community Health
Clunis, Christopher	
Clunis, Christopher	Sister
Davies, Dr Gaius	The Maudsley Hospital
de Coverly, Ivor	Lancelot Andrewes Resettlement Unit
Esposito JP, Angela	Member of Public
Fernando, Dr Suman	Chase Farm Hospital
George, Ferard	Lancelot Andrewes Resettlement Unit
Gill, Inspector Derek	Edmonton Police Station
Gillen, Kieran	HEG, Haringey Social Services
Green, Julian	Haringey Social Services
Gupta, Dr Kamal	Guy's Hospital
Higgitt, Dr Anna	St Charles Hospital
Hislop, Wendy	Member of Public
Jennings, Carol	Haringey Social Services
Kennedy, Dr Henry	Friern Hospital

Kent, Ian	Guy's and St Thomas' Hospital Trust
Korman, Nancy	Haringey Health Care, St Ann's Hospital
Lamb, John	Lancelot Andrewes Resettlement Unit
Lawrence, Joan	Haringey Social Services
Lewis, Janine	Haringey Social Services
Lomax, Dr Steven	Kneesworth House Hospital
McCarthy, Dr Anthony	Guy's Hospital
McLachlan, Dr Adrian	GP (Lancelot Andrewes House)
Murray, Hugh	Lambeth Social Services
Oakeley, Dr Henry	St Thomas' Hospital
Owen, DC Gwynfor	Southwark Police Station
Packer, Martin	St Thomas' Hospital
Parashar, Susan	Member of Public
Parker, Dr Elizabeth	Hither Green Hospital
Parrott, Dr Janet	HMP Belmarsh
Patel, Dr Anant	GP, FHSA (Enfield & Haringey)
Payne, Brian	Haringey Social Services
Pullinger, HH Judge John	Croydon Combined Court
Purse, David	Mental Health Team for Single Homeless People
Rimmer, Anthony	Barrister
Robson, Ursula	Haringey Social Services
Roth, Dr Michael	St Charles Hospital
Scott, Hilary	Enfield & Haringey FHSA
Seacole, Christine	Guy's Hospital
Seargeant, Dr Janet	Friern Hospital
Shepherd, Dr Simon	GP - Rosemead Hostel
Shubsachs, Dr Alexander	Rampton Hospital
Singh, Sean	Nurse, St Thomas' Hospital
Sivakumar, Bala	Lewin Road Mental Health Centre
Sivananthan, Dr Nalliah	GP, FHSA (Enfield & Haringey)
Subrahmanyam, Dr Pasapula	GP, FHSA (Enfield & Haringey)
Sullivan, PC Neville	Edmonton Police Station
Staples, Sergeant John	Edmonton Police Station
Taube, Martin	Christopher Clunis' solicitor
Taylor, John	Lancelot Andrewes Resettlement Unit
Taylor, Dr Sarah	Friern Hospital
Taylor, Stephen	Three Boroughs Primary Healthcare
Townley, Peter	Haringey Social Services
Turner, Roger	Barrister
Tutton, Irene	Jayne Zito's mother

APPENDIX 2

EXPERT WITNESSES AND OTHER INTERESTED PARTIES

ORGANISATION	NAME
Association of Directors of Social Services	* Elizabeth Crowther Dewi Evans
Afro-Caribbean Mental Health Association	* Geraldine Huka
Audit Commission	Andrew Foster * Dr Judith Renshaw
British Assocition of Social Workers	* David Jones * Patty Ducie * Janice Stout
Bracton Clinic	Stephen Page
CPNA	Hilary Grevatt Brian Rogers
Confidential Inquiry into Homicides & Suicides by Mentally Ill People	Dr W D Boyd
Department of Health	* Elizabeth Parker * Dora Pease * Ian Jewesbury
HMP Brixton	V Somasundaram
Holloway Police Station	Detective Inspector Robert Webster
Inner London Probation Service	A J Hearne
Institute of Psychiatry	* Professor David Goldberg
Jaques & Lewis (solicitors)	* Dr David Mathieson
London Borough of Enfield	Maralyn Arnold

The Maudsley (Bethlem Royal)	Dr James A C McKeith
Member of Public	Rhoda Cuningham Phil Gillis P Handley Clive Martin Liz Millbank Eddie Slim
Mental After Care Association	Gil Hitchon
Mental Health Act Commission	* William Bingley * Dr Dorothy Black * Elaine Rassaby
Mental Health Team for Single Homeless People	* Clifford Bean
Mental Welfare Commission for Scotland	* Dr James Dyer
MIND	* Ian Bynoe
NHS Management Executive	Alan Bell
NSF	* Gary Hogman * Dorothy Silberston * Mary Teasdale
Police Policy Unit,	* Sergeant Paul Etheridge
Scotland Yard	* Inspector Christopher Smith
Rampton Hospital	Dr I A P Keitch Tom McNeeney
RCGP	Dr Mollie McBride
RDP	David Martindale Dr Matt Muijen
Royal College of Nursing	* Professor Kevin Gourney Christine Hancock
Royal College of Psychiatrists	* Professor Tom Burns Dr Fiona Caldicott
St Georges Hospital	* Dr Aggrey Burke

St George's Hospital Medical School	* Dr Nigel Eastman
SANE	Hazel Keelan
	* Marjorie Wallace
South East London Health Authority	* Paul Ward
Survivors Speak Out	* David Keay
Three Boroughs Primary	* David Lowe
Health Care Team	* John Balazs
	* Audrey Hayes
Turning Point	Dr Wendy Thomson
Guy's & St Thomas' Medical School	Prof Elaine Murphy
UNISON	Alan Jinkinson
The Volunteer Centre UK	* Andrea Kelmanson
West Lambeth Community Care (NHS) Trust	* Dr David Roy
Senior Prosecuting Counsel to Treasury	* John Nutting QC
	* gave oral evidence

APPENDIX 3

BIBLIOGRAPHY

1955, 7 July National Health Service, **Reporting of Accidents in Hospital**. Ministry of Health, HM(55)66.

1966, 7 March National Health Service, **Methods of Dealing with Complaints by Patients**, Ministry of Health, HM(66)15.

1966, 1 Nov **Report of the Royal Commission on Tribunals of Inquiry**. Chairman: Rt. Hon. Lord Justice Salmon. Cmd 3121.

1973, Jan **Report on the Review of Procedures for the Discharge and Supervision of Psychiatric Patients Subject to Special Restrictions**. Sir Carl Aarvold, Prof. Sir Denis Hill and Mr G.P. Newton. Cmd 5191.

1983 **Mental Health Act, 1983**. HMSO.

1984 **Scottish Home and Health Department Mental Health (Scotland) Act 1984**, Code of Practice.

1984 **Police and Criminal Evidence Act 1984 (s.66): Codes of Practice**.

1985, 30 Jan House of Commons: 2nd Report from the Social Services Committee, Session 1984-85. **Community Care, with special reference to adult mentally ill and mentally handicapped people**. Vol. 1. Report together with the proceedings of the Committee. HMSO.

1985, 4 July House of Commons: Sixth Report from the Social Services Committee, Session 1984-85. **Public Expenditure on the Social Services**. Together with the proceedings of the Committee, the Minutes of Evidence and an Appendix. HMSO.

1985, Nov Department of Health and Social Security, **Government Response to the Second Report from the Social Services Committee, 1984-85 session Community Care, with special reference to adult mentally ill and mentally handicapped people**. Cmnd 9674.

1985 HN(85)2. **Mental Illness: Policies and Priorities**. Annex 1 to the Government's response to the Social Services Committee Report on "Community Care, with special reference to adult mentally ill and mentally handicapped people". Cmd 9674.

1986, Dec Audit Commission. **Making a Reality of Community Care**. HMSO.

1986 **Disabled Persons (Services, Consultation and Representation) Act 1986**. (Extract: Section 7).

1986 **Regina v Hallstrom and Another, Ex parte W; Regina v. Gardener and Another, Ex parte L**. Nov 13, 18, 19. Dec 20. [1986] QB 1090.

1986 **Disabled Persons (Services, Consultation and Representation) Act 1986**.

1987 **Mental Health Act, 1983**. Memorandum on Parts I to VI, VIII and X. HMSO.

1988, 12 Feb **Community Care: Agenda for Action**. A report to the Secretary of State for Social Services by Sir Roy Griffiths. HMSO.

1988, 2 Feb National Unit for Psychiatric Research and Development, **Towards co-ordinated care for people with long-term, severe mental illness**. Report of a working conference held at Robin Brook Centre, St Bartholomew's Hospital, London.

1988, July Department of Health and Social Security HC(88)43/LAC(88)14/FPN(88)457. **Health Services Development Resource Assumptions and Planning Guidelines**.

1988, July Department of Health and Social Security. **Report of the Committee of Inquiry into the care and aftercare of Miss Sharon Campbell**. Chairman: John Spokes QC. Cmd 440. HMSO.

1989, Feb Department of Health, **Discharge of Patients from Hospital**, Health Circular HC(89)5.

1989, Nov Department of Health and Department of Social Security, **Caring for People - Community Care in the Next Decade and Beyond**. Cmd 849.

1988 Department of Health and Social Security, HC(88)43/LAC(88)14/FRN(88)457. **Health Services Development Resource Assumptions and Planning Guidelines**.

1989, 22 Aug NSF, **Comments on Department of Health Draft Circular on the Care Programme Approach**.

1989, Aug Department of Health of Great Britain. **General Practice in the National Health Service: The 1990 Contract**. The Government's programme for changes to GP's terms of service and remuneration system.

1989 **Children Act, 1989**, Guide to Child Protection Procedures.

1989 National Schizophrenia Fellowship, **Housing for People who are severely mentally ill**, edited by Terry Hammond and Pat Wallace.

1989, Jan Department of Health. **Working for Patients. The Health Service: Caring for the 1990s**. Cmd 555.

1989 American Pyschiatric Association, **DSM III R**.

1989 Department of Health Circular HC(89)5. **Discharge of Patients from Hospital, and Guidance Booklet on implementing HC(89)5**.

1989 Department of Health and Welsh Office. **Code of Practice, Mental Health Act, 1983**. Laid before parliament in December 1989 pursuant to section 118(4) of the Mental Health Act 1983. (1st edition).

1990, 1 Jan Cornwall County Council Social Service Department (Adult Services). **Mental Health Act, 1983, Local Policy and Procedures**.

1990, 5 Apr JR, Joseph Rowntree Memorial Trust, **Findings: Safeguarding Standards**.

1990, Aug SEARCH, Joseph Rowntree Memorial Trust, **A Profession at the Crossroads**, Malcolm Dean.

1990, 3 Sept Home Office Circular No 66/90. **Provision for Mentally Disordered Offenders**. Including Annexes A to F.

1990, Oct Brenda Hoggett, QC, **Mental Health Law**, Sweet and Maxwell.

1990, 7 Nov Metropolitan Police Memorandum, **Revised procedures for dealing with people detained under section 136 of the Mental Health Act, 1983**.

1990, Nov Department of Health. **Caring for People: Community Care in the Next Decade and Beyond. Policy Guidance**. Cmd 849.

1990 **The NHS and Community Care Act, 1990, chapter 19**.

1990 David Martindale, **Mental Health Link**. Research and Development in Psychiatry.

1990 British Association of Social Workers: **'Safeguarding Standards' - The BASW Response**.

1990 Department of Health, HC(90)23/LASSL(90)11: Joint Health and Social Services Circular. Health and Social Services Development. **"Caring for People". The Care Programme Approach for People with a Mental Illness referred to the Special Psychiatric Services**.

1990 HC(90)23/LASSL(90)11: **Annex**.

1991, Jan Medical Protection Society, **Consent and Confidentiality**.

1991, Feb General Medical Council, **Professional Conduct and Discipline: Fitness to Practice**.

1991, 30 Apr Letter from North East Thames Regional Health Authority to Department of Health, Regional Liaison re: **Care Programme Approach HC(90)23 in North East Thames RHA**.

1991, 10 May Letter from South East Thames Regional Health Authority to Department of Health re: **Care Programme HC(90)23**.

1991, 24 July EL(91)103. Executive letter from NHS Management Executive to Regional General Managers. **Priorities and Planning Guidance for the NHS for 1992/93.**

1991, Oct Royal College of Psychiatrists: **Good Medical Practice in the Aftercare of Potentially Violent or Vulnerable Patients Discharged from In-Patient Psychiatric Treatment**. Council Report CR12.

1991, Oct Hampshire County Council, Social Services Department, **Mental Health Act Practice Handbook.**

1991, Nov Department of Health and Home Office. **Review of Health and Social Services for Mentally Disordered Offenders and others requiring similar services**. Chairman: Dr John Reed. Volume 2. Service Needs. The reports of the community, hospital and prison advisory groups and on Overview by the Steering Committee.

1991, 13 Mar Letter from Stephen Dorrell, MP, to the Lord Mottistone, **RE: CODE OF PRACTICE: MENTAL HEALTH ACT 1983**.

1991 Reed Committee, **Extract from Reed Committee's Hospital Advisory Group Consultation Paper: Other Local Provision**.

1991 West Midlands RHA, **Report of the Panel of Inquiry Appointed to Investigate the Case of Kim Kirkman**.

1991 NHSME, **Criminal Justice Act, 1991: Mentally disordered offenders** - Health Service Guidelines.

1991 **Criminal Procedure (Insanity and Unfitness to Plead) Act, 1991, Chapter 25.** Current Law Statutes Annotated.

1991 Medical Protection Society. **Disclosure of Medical Records**.

1992, Jan Medical Defence Union Ltd, **Confidentiality**.

1992, 7 Feb Letter from NHS Management Executive to Regional General Managers. **Implementation of Caring for People: Corporate Contracts**.

1992, 18 Feb Department of Health and Welsh Office, Miscellaneous letter (92)16. **Notification of amendment to paragraph 2.6 of the Code of Practice issued under Section 118 of the Mental Health Act 1983**.

1992, 11 Mar Department of Health EL(92)13/CI(92)10. Executive letter from NHS Management Executive/ Social Services Inspectorate. **Implementing Caring for People**.

1992, Mar Haringey Health Authority, **Care Group Schedule for the Provision of Mental Health Services Schedule F9**.

1992, 25 Sept Department of Health. EL(92)65/CI(92)30. Executive letter from NHS Management Executive/ Social Services Inspectorate. **Implementing Caring for People**.

1992, Dec North East Thames Regional Health Authority. **Independent Inquiry into Kevin Rooney**. Chairman: Andrew Collins QC.

1992 Department of Health. **Review of Health and Social Services for Mentally Disordered Offenders and Others Requiring Similar Services**. Chairman: Dr John Reed. Final summary report. Cmd 2088. HMSO.

1992 Medical Protection Society, **Disclosure of Medical Records**.

1992-93 Mental Welfare Commission for Scotland, **Annual Report 1992-93**.

1992-93 Volunteer Centre, UK, **Making an Impact on Volunteering**, Annual Report 1992/93.

1992 North East Thames RHA, **Access to Health, Promoting Health for Homeless People: How to Count Your Homeless Population**.

1993, 25 Jan NSF, Dorothy Silberston, **NSF Stance on Reed Report**.

1993, Jan Home Office: **Report of an unannounced short inspection by HM Inspectorate of Prisons, Brixton Prison**.

1993, Jan Royal College of Psychiatrists. **Evidence to the Health Committee Inquiry into Community Supervision Orders**.

1993, Jan General Medical Council: **Professional Conduct and Discipline: Fitness to Practice**. (Includes guidance on *professional confidence*.)

1993, Jan Access to Health, 1992, **How to Count Your Homeless Population**.

1993, Jan Department of Health, The Health of the Nation, **Key Area Handbook - Mental Illness**.

1993, Jan Lambeth Southwark and Lewisham Family Health Services Authority and South East London Health Authority: **Roots to Health, A Strategy for the Development of Health Care Services for the Homeless**.

1993, Feb CHAR, Housing Campaign for Single People, Joseph Oldman, **Broken Promises - A survey of Resettlement Unit Replacement Packages**.

1993, 10 Mar Meeting in the House of Lords called by the Mathew Trust with the support of the special hospitals service authority, **Patient Privacy versus Private Interest, Press and Patient Confidentiality forum report (Part A), Media Intrusion and the Press Complaints Commission (Part B)**.

1993, Mar Department of Health, LAC(93)7, **Ordinary Residence**, Local Authority Circular.

1993, Mar NHSME **Establishing a District of Residence.**

1993, Mar Resettlement Agency: **Framework Document.**

1993, Mar Royal College of General Practitioners: **Statement of Homelessness and General Practice.**

1993, Mar Department of Social Security, **Care in the Community - Changes in Income Support and other Social Security Benefits from 1 April 1993.**

1993, Apr Department of Health, **Caring for People with Severe Mental Illness, Information for Psychiatrists.**

1993, Apr Access to Health, **Community Mental Health Services and Homeless People.** Draft paper by Access to Health outlining the guidelines on access to services by homeless people who are placed outside their district of origin. For consultation in NETRHA.

1993, Apr Hampshire County Council Social Services Department, Community Care - **Who can get help from Social Services?**

1993, Apr Richard Gordon, **Community Care Assessments: A Practical Legal Framework**, Longman.

1993, 19 May Department of Health and the Welsh Office, **Mental Health Act 1983, Code of Practice**, laid before Parliament on 19 May 1993 pursuant to section 118(4) of the Mental Health Act 1983.

1993, 19 May RDP, **Homelessness and Mental Health Initiative, Second Report to the Mental Health Foundation**, T. Craig, C. Hepworth, O. Klein, P. Manning, M. Ratcliffe.

1993, 19 May BASW, **Response to the Health Committee Inquiry into Community Supervision Orders.**

1993, May Community Psychiatric Nurses' Association, **Evidence to the House of Commons Select Committee on Health Inquiry into Community Supervision Orders.**

1993, May Mental Health Act Commission. **Evidence to the Health Committee Inquiry into Community Supervision Orders.**

1993, May CPNA, **Evidence to the House of Commons Select committee on Health Inquiry into Community Supervision Orders.**

1993, 23 June House of Commons, Session 1992-93. Health Committee 5th Report. **Community Supervision Orders.** Vol.1.1.

1993, June Department of Health, **Factors influencing the Implementation of the Care Programme Approach, and Summary** and **detail.**

1993, June Medical Defence Union Ltd, **Confidentiality.**

144

1993, June North, C and Ritchie J, **Factors Influencing the Implementation of the Care Programme Approach**, A research study carried out for the Department of Health by the Social and Community Planning Research.

1993, June NHSME, **Mental Health Task Force: Progress and Plans**.

1993, 9 July **Transcript of Crampton & Ors v. Secretary of State for Health**. (The Beverley Allitt case).

1993, 31 July The Lancet: **Suicide after discharge from psychiatric inpatient care**. Vol. 342.

1993, July Department of Health, The Health of the Nation, **Mental Illness: What does it mean?** Prepared by the Department of Health and produced by Creese and Associates.

1993, July **Community Care: The housing dimension**. Peter Arnold, Hugh Bochel, Sally Broadhurst and Dilys Page. Community Care into Practice.

1993, 4 Aug EL(93)68. **Assessment of need for services for mentally disordered offenders and others with similar needs**. NHS Management Executive.

1993, 10 Aug Research and Development for Psychiatry, Mental Health Link, **Version 3.0, Care Manager**.

1993, 12 Aug Department of Health. **Letter announcing "The Ten Point Plan", and press release**.

1993, Aug The Medical Defence Union Ltd, **Can I see the records?**

1993, Aug Department of Health. **Legal Powers on the Care of Mentally Ill People in the Community**.

1993, Aug Department of Health and Welsh Office. **Code of Practice, Mental Health Act 1983**. Published August 1993 pursuant to section 118(4) of the Mental Health Act 1983. (2nd edition).

1993, 15 Sept NSF, **Reed Committee - Consultation Papers: Recommendations by Hospital Advisory Group Response by National Schizophrenia Fellowship**.

1993, Sept BASW, **Response to the Health Committee Inquiry into Mental Health Services**.

1993, Sept Community Psychiatric Nurses' Association, **Evidence to the House of Commons Select Committee on Health Inquiry into Mental Health Services**.

1993, 3 Oct BASW, **The Recommendations of the Internal Review**, Mike Cox.

1993, 4 Oct NHSME, **Criminal Justice Act 1991: Mentally Disordered Offenders**.

1993, 17 Oct NSF, Letter to Michael O'Connor, the Secretariat, Mental Health Legislation Review Team, Department of Health from Dorothy Silberston, Vice-Chairman NSF. **Secretary of State's 10 Point Plan and Review Team's Report on Legal Powers for the Care of Mentally Ill People in the Community**.

1993, 17 Oct **NSF, NSF's Detailed Comments on Proposals for an Extension of Leave Under the Act from 6 months to 1 year and for the Supervised Discharge.**

1993, 19 Oct BASW, **Legal Powers on the Care of Mentally Ill People in the Community**.

1993, Oct **Unison response to the Department of Health Consultation on "Legal Powers on the Care of the Mentally Ill People in the Community - Report of the Internal Review"**.

1993, 13 Nov British Medical Journal, **Information Management and Patient Privacy in the NHS**: Written by Alison Tanks.

1993, Nov Law Commission, **Legislating the Criminal Code. Offences Against the Person and General Principles**, Cmnd 2370.

1993, Nov Institute of Psychiatry and the Department of General Practice, UMDS: **Developing a Strategy for a Primary Care Focus for Mental Health Services**. David Goldberg, Anthony Mann, David Pilgrim, Anne Rogers, Debbie Sharp, Kim Sutherby, Geraldine Strathdee, Graham Thornicroft and Til Wykes.

1993, 21 Dec Jeremy W. Coid, **A survey of Bed Occupancy in Medium Security, 21st November, 1993**. Discussion paper for the Department of Health.

1993, Dec The Mental Health Act Commission, **Fifth Biennial Report, 1991-1993**, laid before Parliament by the Secretary of State for Health pursuant to Section 121(10) of the Mental Health Act 1993.

1993 Dr Dick Thompson, **The Mental Health Foundation, Mental Illness the Fundamental Facts**.

1993 The Law Commission, Consultation Paper No. 130. **Mentally Incapacitated Adults and Other Vulnerable Adults. Public Law Protection. HMSO.**

1993 Special Hospitals Service Authority. **Report of the Committee of Inquiry into the death of Broadmoor Hospital or Orville Blackwood and a Review of the Deaths of Two other Afro-caribbean Patients. "Big, Black and Dangerousness?"** Chairman: Professor Herschel Prins.

1993 Department of Health, The Health of the Nation, **Mental Illness: A guide to mental health in the workplace**, edited by R. Jenkins and D. Warman. HMSO.

1993 Department of Health, The Health of the Nation, **Mental Illness: Sometimes I think I can't go on any more...**, produced by Creese & Associates.

Printed in the United Kingdom for HMSO.
Dd.0297831, 5/94, C10, 3400, 5673, 288019.